70s
POP GENIUS
QUIZ BOOK

CLARKSDALE

Can you name the three centre silhouettes? Answers on our blog at www.clarksdalebooks.co.uk

CLARKSDALE

Published by Clarksdale, an imprint of Ovolo Books Ltd
Text © David Roberts 2011
This edition © Ovolo Books Ltd 2011

Publisher: Mark Neeter
Cover design concept: Poppublishing
Proof reading: Matthew White

ISBN: 978 1 9059593 6 5
Printed in the UK

www.clarksdalebooks.co.uk

Thanks to: Martin Downham, John Butters, Chris Butters, Julian Knight, Rob Dimery, David Jones, Janet Roberts, Dave McAleer, Dave Okomah, Brian Southall

70s POP GENIUS QUIZ BOOK

Compiled by
DAVID ROBERTS

INTRODUCTION

Some people find it fun, some people take it more seriously, but whether pop quizzes are obsessive brain-bending torture or just a good night of friendly competition for you, here are 1000 carefully compiled questions with a range of difficulty for every occasion.

Designed to stretch the boundaries of your pop knowledge that little bit further, you can play the 200 themed quizzes individually or take our Pop Genius challenge and see how many points you can total from the 5,000 on offer.

The answers to all questions are cunningly printed on the outside column of the page directly behind the quiz page you're looking at. The answers are therefore always two pages after the quiz – so the answers to the quiz on page 15 are on page 17 and so on.

ARE YOU A POP GENIUS?

Want to rate yourself? Obviously it's only our opinion, but after much poptastic assessment and non-scientific research we reckon that these are the degrees of pop cleverness you will have achieved...

2000 points: You are the owner of a good, solid knowledge of pop and would not disgrace any self-respecting pop quiz team down the local pub or club.

3000 points: You are the envy of your friends and regularly astound them with your ability to correctly answer just about any pop question thrown at you.

4000 points: You possess a pop knowledge probably unrivalled by anyone you know or in your local vicinity. Bordering on Genius status.

4500 to 5000 points: You are quite simply Pop Genius material and can award yourself the title of Pop Professor at the highest University of popular music. And should you prove a claim that you have managed to bag 4900 points we'd love to hear from you. As a result we will endeavour to put you in touch with anyone, unlikely as it seems, in your league of pop knowledgeability. Who knows, we might even be able to identify and crown the undisputed heavyweight pop quiz champion of the UK and Ireland.

And before I leave you to tuck into the 1000 questions, here's one to introduce you to the sort of fiendish stuff that follows…

What do Emmylou Harris, 75p, the sc-fi movie 'Village Of The Damned', Carly Simon, 'The St. Cleve Chronicle and Linwell Advertiser' and Farrah Fawcett have in common? Answer: they are the answers to the questions posed on the back cover of this book!

AUTHOR'S NOTES

All questions and answers in the 'Seventies Pop Genius Quiz Book' refer to UK chart data unless otherwise specified.

Any similarity between the content of this book and the superlative pop publishing activity of Tim Rice, Jonathan Rice and Paul Gambaccini is no coincidence!

This author is indebted to the inspiration gained down the years as editor and willing apprentice to all three pop geniuses, with whom he worked on The Guinness Book of British Hit Singles, Hit Albums and many more excellent and hugely popular reference books.

David Roberts

SOLO BEATLES

The most successful and popular group of all-time might have recorded their last music together in 1969, but huge solo success for John, Paul, George and Ringo continued in the 70s.

IMPORTANT

The answers to all questions are cunningly printed on the outside column of the page directly behind the quiz page you're looking at. The answers are therefore always two pages after the quiz – so the answers to this quiz are on page 8. (Stop! Don't turn and look until you've done the quiz - they are there, we promise you!)

QUESTION 1 *(5 POINTS)*

The UK's biggest-selling single of the 70s, 'Mull Of Kintyre', was a double A-Side - but which track was on the flip side?

a 'Girls' School'
b 'Give Ireland Back To The Irish'
c 'C Moon'

QUESTION 2 *(5 POINTS)*

Which location played host to George Harrison's Concert For Bangladesh in 1971?

a Madison Square Garden, New York
b Wembley Stadium, London
c Hyde Park, London

QUESTION 3 *(5 POINTS)*

What was the name of Ringo's own record label founded in 1975?

a Restless Records
b Ring O'Records
c Storm Records

QUESTION 4 *(5 POINTS)*

In 1971 John Lennon and Yoko Ono moved from which Georgian manor house to live in the USA?

a Tittenhurst Park
b Hillary Mansions
c Mendips

QUESTION 5 *(5 POINTS)*

George Harrison appears on the cover of his album All Things Must Pass wearing what on his feet?

a Carpet slippers
b Wellington boots
c Nothing

PUNK FIRSTS

It came, it saw, it conquered in double quick time. Here are five questions about those at the vanguard of the punk movement.

IMPORTANT

QUESTION 1 *(5 POINTS)*
What is generally accepted to be the first single release of the punk era?
a 'Anarchy In The UK' by the Sex Pistols
b 'White Riot' by The Clash
c 'New Rose' by The Damned

QUESTION 2 *(5 POINTS)*
What was the title of the first and only hit album by The Slits?
a Cut
b Splice
c Prick

QUESTION 3 *(5 POINTS)*
With whom did the Sex Pistols first sign a record contract?
a EMI
b Virgin
c Stiff

QUESTION 4 *(5 POINTS)*
Which of these three radio presenters was a writer on the pioneering punk fanzine Sniffin' Glue?
a Simon Mayo
b Jeremy Vine
c Danny Baker

QUESTION 5 *(5 POINTS)*
Now commemorated by a wall plaque, where was the London location of the Sex Pistols' first ever gig?
a The London School Of Economics
b St. Martin's School Of Art
c The Hope & Anchor public house

The answers to all questions are cunningly printed on the outside column of the page directly behind the quiz page you're looking at. The answers are therefore always two pages after the quiz – so the answers to this quiz are on page 9. (Stop! Don't turn and look until you've done the quiz - they are there, we promise you!)

WEIRD LYRICS

The points are only yours if you manage to name both the song and the artist correctly.

QUIZ 001

Q1
What was the flip side of 'Mull Of Kintyre'?
a 'Girls' School'

Q2
Location of the Concert For Bangladesh?
a Madison Square Garden, New York

Q3
Name of Ringo's own record label?
b Ring O'Records

Q4
Name of UK house John and Yoko moved from in 1971?
a Tittenhurst Park

Q5
George Harrison's footwear on All Things Must Pass?
b Wellington boots

QUESTION 1 *(4 POINTS)*
Which 70s Top 10 hit describes "cellophane flowers" and "newspaper taxis"?

QUESTION 2 *(4 POINTS)*
Which 1978 No.1 begins with the words "I was walkin' down the street, Concentrating on truckin' right", and which act had a hit with it?

QUESTION 3 *(7 POINTS)*
The colour of the composer also features in the title of this Top 10 hit, which begins "Now, when the day goes to sleep and the full moon looks. The night is so black that the darkness cooks." Name the song and the act responsible.

QUESTION 4 *(5 POINTS)*
Work out the song and the act who went Top 10 with these lyrics. "If we're going down the pub, you'd better tell your mum and dad, and finish up your grub."

QUESTION 5 *(5 POINTS)*
Lyrics don't come much weirder than these from this British male vocal / instrumental group. Name the song and the act. "Commanded, I was branded in a plastic vac. Surrounded and confounded by statistic facts."

WHEN WAS THAT?

Recall these moments in time? As always, 25 points are yours if you do.

QUESTION 1 *(5 POINTS)*

In which year did Barbra Streisand's 'Stoney End' single and album of the same name first hit the UK chart?

a 1971

b 1972

c 1973

QUESTION 2 *(5 POINTS)*

Select the correct single that had the distinction of being the last No.1 single of the 70s (and first of the 80s).

a 'Eye Of The Tiger' by Survivor

b 'Another Brick In The Wall (Part 2) by Pink Floyd

c 'Do They Know It's Christmas? by Band Aid

QUESTION 3 *(5 POINTS)*

In which year did Eagles band member Joe Walsh enjoy his biggest UK solo hit single with 'Life's Been Good'?

a 1972

b 1975

c 1978

QUESTION 4 *(5 POINTS)*

Which month of the year featured in a1978 Earth, Wind And Fire hit?

a January

b September

c December

QUESTION 5 *(5 POINTS)*

'Mama Weer All Crazee Now' by Slade was No.1 on 21 September and Oasis' Liam Gallagher was born the same day. Name the year.

a 1972

b 1974

c 1976

Q1
First single release of the punk era?
c 'New Rose' by The Damned

Q2
What was the title of the first and only hit album by The Slits?
a Cut

Q3
With whom did the Sex Pistols first sign a record contract?
a EMI

Q4
Radio presenter who wrote for punk fanzine Sniffin' Glue?
c Danny Baker

Q5
London location of the Sex Pistols' first ever gig?
b St. Martin's School Of Art

QUIZ 003

REAL NAMES

They weren't born pop stars. These five even needed to discard their former selves before making an impact.

Q1
The song in question?
'Lucy In The Sky With Diamonds' by Elton John

Q2
1978 No.1 begins "I was walkin' down the street"
'Dreadlock Holiday' by 10CC

Q3
Hit begins: "Now, when the day goes to sleep..."
'Green Manalishi' by Fleetwood Mac

Q4
The pub hit in question?
'Hurry Up Harry' by Sham 69

Q5
"Commanded, I was branded in a plastic vac"
'Son Of My Father' by Chicory Tip

QUESTION 1 *(5 POINTS)*
Which of these three was the name Cockney Rebel frontman Steve Harley was given by his parents?
a Stephen Smiley
b Steven Nice
c Steven Hasselhoff

QUESTION 2 *(5 POINTS)*
Choose the correct name for the New Yorker who became Aerosmith front man Steven Tyler.
a Raymond Tabano
b Steven Perry
c Steven Tallarico

QUESTION 3 *(5 POINTS)*
Choose which of these three names appeared on heartthrob David Essex's birth certificate?
a David Albert Cook
b Glen William Clacton
c Christopher Robert Harlow

QUESTION 4 *(5 POINTS)*
Ozzy Osbourne isn't the original name of the heavy metal icon. Which of these is the Birmingham-born hell-raiser's real moniker?
a Edward Oliver Osbourne
b John Michael Osbourne
c Paul Francis Fowler

QUESTION 5 *(5 POINTS)*
Freeport Long Island was the birthplace of rock transformer Lou Reed. But what is his real name?
a Louis Allen Firbank
b Arthur Noel
c Douglas Leslie Lee

SATURDAY NIGHT/ SUNDAY MORNING

QUIZ 004

Your weekend questions start here...

QUESTION 1 *(2 POINTS)*
From which studio album did the Elton John single 'Saturday Night's Alright For Fighting' come?
a Don't Shoot Me I'm Only The Piano Player
b Goodbye Yellow Brick Road
c Caribou

QUESTION 2 *(3 POINTS)*
In which year did Blondie's 'Sunday Girl' top the chart?
a 1977
b 1978
c 1979

QUESTION 3 *(6 POINTS)*
Who had an exotic weekend in 1979 with 'Saturday Night (Beneath The Plastic Palm Trees)'?
a 10cc
b Dr Feelgood
c The Leyton Buzzards

QUESTION 4 *(7 POINTS)*
Which of these three folk legends released a 70s album titled Sunday's Child?
a Donovan
b John Martyn
c Sandy Denny

QUESTION 5 *(7 POINTS)*
Tom Waits' critically-acclaimed second album was called what?
a The Heart Of Saturday Night
b Saturday Night In San Francisco
c Pomona Sunday

Q1
Which year did 'Stoney End' single and album first chart in UK?
a 1971

Q2
Last No.1 of the 70s (and 80s first)
b 'Another Brick In The Wall (Part 2)' by Pink Floyd

Q3
Year 'Life's Been Good' hit the UK chart?
c 1978

Q4
Which month of the year featured in a 1978 Earth, Wind And Fire hit?
b September

Q5
Year 'Mama Weer All Crazee Now' hit No 1 and Liam Gallagher born?
a 1972

QUIZ 007 SEVENTIES POP GENIUS

DID THEY OR DIDN'T THEY?

A series of true or false statements about rock and pop facts.

Q1
**Real name of
Cockney Rebel
frontman Steve
Harley?**
b Steven Nice

QUESTION 1 *(5 POINTS)*
**Shakin' Stevens was the UK singles chart's most successful
performer in the 80s but had no hits in the 70s.**
a True
b False

Q2
**Correct name
for Aerosmith
frontman Steven
Tyler?**
c Steven Tallarico

QUESTION 2 *(5 POINTS)*
'Get Back' was a 70s Top 20 hit for Rod Stewart.
a True
b False

Q3
**Name on David
Essex's birth
certificate?**
a David Albert Cook

QUESTION 3 *(5 POINTS)*
US musicians Edgar Winter and Johnny Winter are brothers.
a True
b False

Q4
**Ozzy's full
name?**
b John Michael
Osbourne

QUESTION 4 *(5 POINTS)*
Singer-songwriter Gilbert O'Sullivan was born in New Zealand.
a True
b False

Q5
**Lou Reed began
life as?**
a Louis Allen
Firbank

QUESTION 5 *(5 POINTS)*
**Eugene Record was the name of the lead vocalist for the US act
The Chi-Lites**
a True
b False

WHERE YOU FROM?

Pop location, location, location with the usual 25 points at stake.

QUIZ 008

QUESTION 1 *(4 POINTS)*

Which country gave birth to rockers Boston?

a USA

b Canada

c UK

QUESTION 2 *(4 POINTS)*

Name the town in Indiana where Michael Jackson was born.

a Shirley

b Lawrence

c Gary

QUESTION 3 *(7 POINTS)*

The Golden Torch was a legendary mid-60s to mid-70s Northern Soul venue based in which of these industrial hotspots?

a Wigan

b Macclesfield

c Stoke-on-Trent

QUESTION 4 *(5 POINTS)*

If Police's Sting was a Geordie and guitarist Andy Summers was from Lancashire, where did drummer Stewart Copeland spring from?

a California, USA

b Virginia, USA

c Cairo, Egypt

QUESTION 5 *(5 POINTS)*

The glam rock innovator Marc Bolan died in a car crash near which London location?

a Golders Green

b Barnes Common

c The Hammersmith Flyover

Q1

'Saturday Night's Alright For Fighting' is from

b Goodbye Yellow Brick Road

Q2

In which year did Blondie's 'Sunday Girl' top the chart?

c 1979

Q3

The 'Saturday Night' band were

c The Leyton Buzzards

Q4

The folk legend in question?

b John Martyn

Q5

Tom Waits' acclaimed second album?

a The Heart Of Saturday Night

13

MIND THE GAP

Each of these five 70s track titles include a gap you need to fill. Select the correct word to complete the song titles…

QUIZ 007

Q1
Shakin' Stevens - most successful in the 80s but no hits in the 70s.
a True

Q2
'Get Back' was a 70s Top 20 hit for Rod Stewart
a True

Q3
Edgar Winter and Johnny Winter are brothers
a True

Q4
Gilbert O'Sullivan was born in New Zealand
b False. He was born in Ireland

Q5
Eugene Record was lead vocalist for The Chi-Lites
a True

QUESTION 1 *(6 POINTS)*
Manfred Mann's Earth Band's '_____ On The Road Again'
a 'Davey's'
b 'Michael's'
c 'Dylan's'

QUESTION 2 *(6 POINTS)*
St. Cecilia's 'Leap Up And Down (Wave Your _____ In The Air)'
a 'Hands'
b 'Hankies'
c 'Knickers'

QUESTION 3 *(3 POINTS)*
The Who's '_____ Box'
a 'Juke'
b 'Strong'
c 'Squeeze'

QUESTION 4 *(5 POINTS)*
Roy 'C's '_____ Wedding'
a 'White, White'
b 'Shotgun'
c 'Summer Country'

QUESTION 5 *(5 POINTS)*
The Ramones' '_____ Is A Punk Rocker'
a 'Cherry'
b 'Sheila'
c 'Sheena'

NAME THAT GROUP

Just one straight choice required here. A series of names - all you have to do is decide who they are called collectively.

QUESTION 1 *(4 POINTS)*
Steve Marriott, Peter Frampton, Greg Ridley, Jerry Shirley

QUESTION 2 *(4 POINTS)*
Gene Simmons, Paul Stanley, Ace Frehley, Peter Criss

QUESTION 3 *(4 POINTS)*
Justin Hayward, John Lodge, Ray Thomas, Graeme Edge

QUESTION 4 *(7 POINTS)*
'Ron Nasty', 'Stig O'Hara', 'Dirk McQuickly', 'Barry Wom'

QUESTION 5 *(6 POINTS)*
Victor Willis, Felipe Rose, David 'Scar' Hodo, Alexander Briley, Randy Jones, Glenn M. Hughes

QUIZ 008

Q1
Which country gave birth to rockers Boston?
a USA

Q2
Name the town in Indiana where Michael Jackson was born
c Gary

Q3
The Golden Torch was in which industrial hotspot?
c Stoke-on-Trent

Q4
Police drummer Stewart Copeland sprang from
b Virginia, USA

Q5
Marc Bolan died near which London location?
b Barnes Common

15

QUIZ 011 SEVENTIES POP GENIUS

LOVE THAT LABEL

Identify the correct record label that sat in the middle of these seminal 70s singles.

Q1

Manfred Mann's Earth Band's '_____ On The Road Again'
a Davey's

QUESTION 1 *(5 POINTS)*

'Ride A White Swan' by T. Rex
a Elektra
b Fly
c Rocket

Q2

St. Cecilia's 'Leap Up And Down (Wave Your _____ In The Air)'
c 'Knickers'

QUESTION 2 *(5 POINTS)*

'Indiana Wants Me' by R. Dean Taylor
a Tamla Motown
b President
c Trojan

Q3

The Who's '_____ Box'
c 'Squeeze'

QUESTION 3 *(5 POINTS)*

'Won't Get Fooled Again' by The Who
a Mercury
b Track
c Chrysalis

Q4

Roy 'C's '_____ Wedding'
b 'Shotgun'

QUESTION 4 *(5 POINTS)*

'I Shot The Sheriff' by Eric Clapton
a CBS
b EMI
c RSO

Q5

The Ramones' '_____ Is A Punk Rocker'
c 'Sheena'

QUESTION 5 *(5 POINTS)*

'Bye Bye Baby' by the Bay City Rollers
a Bell
b A&M
c Pye

16

DYLANOLOGY

His Bobness has a devoted fan base. If you are a fan, these five will be a walk in the park.

QUIZ 010

QUESTION 1 *(4 POINTS)*
The 70s was arguably Bob Dylan's most commercially successful period and also saw him publish his first book. What was the title?
a Praying Mantis
b Watching The River Flow
c Tarantula

QUESTION 2 *(4 POINTS)*
Who directed the movie Pat Garrett And Billy The Kid in which Dylan appeared?
a Sam Peckinpah
b Martin Scorsese
c Bob Dylan

QUESTION 3 *(7 POINTS)*
Self Portrait was the first of how many UK Top 10 albums by Dylan in the 70s?
a 4
b 8
c 11

QUESTION 4 *(5 POINTS)*
In what year did Dylan's Rolling Thunder Revue first hit the road?
a 1975
b 1977
c 1979

QUESTION 5 *(5 POINTS)*
Only one of these three musicians appeared with Dylan on the Rolling Thunder Revue tour. Which one?
a Eric Clapton
b Mick Ronson
c Tom Petty

Q1
Steve Marriott, Peter Frampton, Greg Ridley, Jerry Shirley =
Humble Pie

Q2
Gene Simmons, Paul Stanley, Ace Frehley, Peter Criss =
Kiss

Q3
Justin Hayward, John Lodge, Ray Thomas, Graeme Edge =
The Moody Blues

Q4
'Ron Nasty', 'Stig O'Hara', 'Dirk McQuickly', 'Barry Wom' =
The Rutles

Q5
Willis, Rose, Hodo, Briley, Jones, Hughes =
The Village People

17

QUIZ 013 SEVENTIES POP GENIUS

WRITTEN BY WHO?

Who wrote what, with some famous names in the frame.

Q1
'Ride A White Swan' by T. Rex
b Fly

Q2
'Indiana Wants Me' by R. Dean Taylor
a Tamla Motown

Q3
'Won't Get Fooled Again' by The Who
b Track

Q4
'I Shot The Sheriff' by Eric Clapton'
c RSO

Q5
'Bye Bye Baby' by the Bay City Rollers
a Bell

QUESTION 1 *(5 POINTS)*

Who was the songwriter responsible for 'Lovin' You' by Minnie Riperton?

a Stevie Wonder

b Minnie Riperton

c Carole King

QUESTION 2 *(6 POINTS)*

Name the wordsmith who created Lena Martell's chart-topper 'One Day At A Time'.

a Dolly Parton

b Kris Kristofferson

c Harry Nilsson

QUESTION 3 *(4 POINTS)*

'If' was a No.1 hit for Telly Savalas, but who wrote the words for one of the shortest-titled UK hit singles?

a Long John Baldry

b David Gates

c Robin Gibb

QUESTION 4 *(4 POINTS)*

Roy Wood's band Wizzard were top of the UK singles chart for four weeks in 1973 with 'See My Baby Jive', which was penned by who?

a Dave Edmunds

b Roy Wood

c Chuck Berry

QUESTION 5 *(6 POINTS)*

Select the correct writer for the Matthews' Southern Comfort autumn 1970 No.1 'Woodstock'.

a Neil Young

b Joni Mitchell

c Bob Dylan

SEVENTIES POP GENIUS QUIZ 014

TOGETHER WE ARE...?

From the names provided decide who they are called together.

QUESTION 1 *(3 POINTS)*
Donald Fagen and Walter Becker

QUESTION 2 *(4 POINTS)*
Brian Connolly, Andy Scott, Steve Priest, Mick Tucker

QUESTION 3 *(7 POINTS)*
Danny Hutton, Chuck Negron, Cory Wells, Mike Allsup, Joe Schermie, Floyd Sneed, Jimmy Greenspoon

---

QUESTION 4 *(8 POINTS)*
Dan McCafferty, Manny Charlton, Pete Agnew, Darrell Sweet

QUESTION 5 *(3 POINTS)*
Billy Gibbons, Dusty Hill, Frank Beard

QUIZ 015 SEVENTIES POP GENIUS

BETTER KNOWN AS...

Five music stars who rejected or changed the names they were born with.

QUESTION 1 *(4 POINTS)*

Which of these three started life as Marvin Lee Aday?
a Meat Loaf
b Marvin Gaye
c Smokey Robinson

QUESTION 2 *(5 POINTS)*

Nashville's Charles Hatcher made a bright future for himself, but what stage name did he perform under?
a Willie Nelson
b Isaac Hayes
c Edwin Starr

QUESTION 3 *(6 POINTS)*

Names don't come much grander: who is Ingram Cecil Connor III?
a Mike Nesmith
b Gram Parsons
c Barry Manilow

QUESTION 4 *(7 POINTS)*

Who is Christopher John Davidson?
a Chris De Burgh
b Christopher Cross
c Joe Strummer

QUESTION 5 *(3 POINTS)*

David Robert Jones swapped this very British name for one of the following.
a Robert Plant
b Brian Eno
c David Bowie

Q1
Who was the responsible for 'Lovin' You' by Minnie Riperton?
a Stevie Wonder

Q2
Who created Lena Martell's chart-topper 'One Day At A Time'?
b Kris Kristofferson

Q3
'If' was written by?
b David Gates

Q4
'See My Baby Jive' was penned by?
b Roy Wood

Q5
Writer of 'Woodstock'?
b Joni Mitchell

ALL ABOUT ABBA

The quartet get a quiz all to themselves. 25 easy points surely for any fan.

QUIZ 014

QUESTION 1 *(5 POINTS)*
The group's name was also the name of one of Sweden's leading businesses. What was the company famous for?
a Wooden clogs
b Wooden kit houses
c Canned fish

QUESTION 2 *(4 POINTS)*
'Waterloo' by Abba won the Eurovision Song Contest for Sweden in 1974, but in which venue and city did the event take place?
a The Brighton Dome
b The Albert Hall, London
c Television Centre, London

QUESTION 3 *(7 POINTS)*
Abba's 'Chiquitita' made a significant impact in which way?
a The hit was the first to make the top of their own Swedish chart.
b The hit was the first the quartet recorded following their divorces.
c The proceeds of sale were donated to UNICEF for the International Year Of The Child.

QUESTION 4 *(4 POINTS)*
Three Swedes and one Norwegian. Increasing your odds with only three choices, who was born in Norway?
a Benny Andersson
b Bjorn Ulvaeus
c Frida Lyngstad

QUESTION 5 *(5 POINTS)*
Which of these Andersons is the correct Abba manager and sometime songwriter?
a Stig Anderson
b Tim Anderson
c Aby Anderson

Q1
Donald Fagen and Walter Becker =
Steely Dan

Q2
Brian Connolly, Andy Scott, Steve Priest, Mick Tucker =
The Sweet

Q3
Hutton, Negron, Wells, Allsup, Schermie, Sneed, Greenspoon =
Three Dog Night

Q4
McCafferty, Charlton, Agnew, Sweet =
Nazareth

Q5
Billy Gibbons, Dusty Hill, Frank Beard =
ZZ Top

QUIZ 015

ULTIMATE ONE-HiT WONDERS

Everything relates to acts who achieved one single UK chart hit - a No.1.

Q1

Marvin Lee Aday became

a Meat Loaf

Q2

Nashville's Charles Hatcher was

c Edwin Starr

Q3

Ingram Cecil Connor III?

b Gram Parsons

Q4

Christopher John Davidson is

a Chris De Burgh

Q5

David Robert Jones swapped his very British name for

c David Bowie

QUESTION 1 *(7 POINTS)*

Who supplied backing vocals to Brian & Michael's 'Matchstalk Men And Matchstalk Cats And Dogs'?

a Mike Harding

b St. Winifred's School Choir

c The cast of Coronation Street

QUESTION 2 *(4 POINTS)*

Give the full names of 'Uptown Top Ranking' chart-toppers Althia & Donna.

a Althea Forrest and Donna Reid

b Althea Woodman and Donna James

c Althea Flowers and Donna Waltham

QUESTION 3 *(3 POINTS)*

In which January did Clive Dunn's 'Grandad' become a one-hit wonder?

a 1971

b 1974

c 1977

QUESTION 4 *(4 POINTS)*

'Eye Level' provided the Simon Park Orchestra with fleeting chart success and provided the theme to which 70s TV series?

a Shoestring

b Van Der Valk

c The Rockford Files

QUESTION 5 *(7 POINTS)*

'No Charge' was an ultimate one-hit wonder for which of these three solo artists?

a Billy Connolly

b Tammy Wynette

c J.J. Barrie

SEVENTIES POP GENIUS  QUIZ 018

ALL TOGETHER NOW

Just one straight choice required here. A series of names - all you have to do is decide who they are called collectively...

QUESTION 1 *(3 POINTS)*
Jon Anderson, Steve Howe, Chris Squire, Alan White, Rick Wakeman

---

QUESTION 2 *(7 POINTS)*
Maurice White, Philip Bailey, Verdine White, Ralph Johnson

QUESTION 3 *(3 POINTS)*
Lionel Richie, Thomas McClary, Milan Williams, William King, Ronald LaPread, Walter 'Clyde' Orange

---

QUESTION 4 *(7 POINTS)*
Maire Brennan, Pol Brennan, Ciaran Brennan, Padraig Duggan, Noel Duggan

---

QUESTION 5 *(5 POINTS)*
Pete Shelley, Steve Diggle, Steve Garvey, John Maher

Q1
Abba's Swedish company business was famous for
c Canned fish

Q2
Abba's 'Waterloo' venue was
a The Brighton Dome

Q3
'Chiquitita'?
c Sales donated to UNICEF for the International Year Of The Child

Q4
Born in Norway?
c Frida Lyngstad

Q5
The correct Abba manager and sometime songwriter?
a Stig Anderson

23

QUIZ 017

70s MILESTONES

Five questions for five key events during the decade.

Q1

**Backing vocals
were by**
b St. Winifred's
School Choir

Q2

**Althia & Donna
were**
a Althea Forrest
and Donna Reid

Q3

**'Grandad'
became a one-
hit wonder in**
a 1971

Q4

**The 70s TV
series was**
b Van Der Valk

Q5

**'No Charge' was
an ultimate one
hit wonder for**
c J.J. Barrie

QUESTION 1 *(8 POINTS)*

**In which year did UK singles sales hit an all-time high of almost
90 million copies?**
a 1970
b 1975
c 1979

QUESTION 2 *(3 POINTS)*

**"The longer he's gone, the more young people appreciate his art.
What's Going On was a work of genius" Janet Jackson on ..?**
a John Lennon
b Marvin Gaye
c James Brown

QUESTION 3 *(4 POINTS)*

**The Idiot and Lust For Life were two 1977 milestone releases
for which of these legends?**
a The Ramones
b Patti Smith
c Iggy Pop

QUESTION 4 *(4 POINTS)*

**Which of these three dates marked the sad passing of the
greatest rock and roll icon of the 20th century, Elvis Presley?**
a 16 August 1977
b 30 April 1978
c 13 August 1978

QUESTION 5 *(6 POINTS)*

**Which Beatle was the first to leave the group permanently in 1970,
prompting the break-up of the most famous group in history?**
a John Lennon
b Ringo Starr
c Paul McCartney

POP GO THE MOVIES

25 points to anyone with a decent general knowledge of a meeting between two worlds of entertainment.

QUIZ 018

QUESTION 1 *(5 POINTS)*
Everyone knows Watership Down included the chart-topping 'Bright Eyes' by Art Garfunkel, but who wrote the book?
a Douglas Adams
b Richard Adams
c Kenneth Graham

Q1
Anderson, Howe, Squire, White, Wakeman =
Yes

QUESTION 2 *(5 POINTS)*
Which of these 70s movie-related releases is the best-selling soundtrack album of all-time with sales of more than 30 million?
a Grease
b Saturday Night Fever
c Paint Your Wagon

Q2
White, Bailey, White, Johnson =
Earth, Wind & Fire

QUESTION 3 *(5 POINTS)*
Which cinematically-named artist had a 1976 hit with 'Movie Star'?
a Harpo
b Garbo
c Hitchcock

Q3
Richie, McClary, Williams, King, LaPread, Orange =
The Commodores

QUESTION 4 *(5 POINTS)*
Who composed the 'shark theme' tune to the oceanic thriller Jaws?
a John Williams
b Henry Mancini
c Marvin Hamlisch

Q4
Brennan, Brennan, Brennan, Duggan, Duggan =
Clannad

QUESTION 5 *(5 POINTS)*
Stardust the movie featured David Essex. What was the name of the rock star character he played in the Michael Apted-directed film?
a Billy McShane
b Jim Maclaine
c Davie McGrain

Q5
Shelley, Diggle, Garvey, Maher =
Buzzcocks

QUIZ 019

TALKING 'BOUT MY GENERATION

Some famous and not-so-famous quotes from rock's great and good.

Q1

UK singles sales hit an all-time high in
c 1979

Q2

Janet Jackson was talking about
b Marvin Gaye

Q3

The legend in question was
c Iggy Pop

Q4

The date in question?
a 16 August 1977

Q5

The first Beatle to leave the group?
c Paul McCartney

QUESTION 1 *(7 POINTS)*

"I didn't even know the 'Summer Of Love' was happening. I was too busy playing with my Action Man." Said which of these punks?
a Joe Strummer
b Captain Sensible
c Sid Vicious

QUESTION 2 *(4 POINTS)*

Which of these three shy, retiring types said: "The reason we're successful, darling? My overall charisma, of course."
a Freddie Mercury
b Diana Ross
c Johnny Rotten

QUESTION 3 *(4 POINTS)*

Who's this talking about certain of his fellow band members? "I think the only ones who didn't have an affair were me and Mick."
a Charlie Watts
b John McVie
c Joe Strummer

QUESTION 4 *(4 POINTS)*

"It's 106 miles to Chicago. We've got a full tank of gas and half a pack of cigarettes. It's dark and we're wearing sunglasses." said who?
a Simon and Garfunkel
b The Blues Brothers
c Sha Na Na

QUESTION 5 *(6 POINTS)*

Who said: "I hope we're a nice old couple living on the coast of Ireland or something like that – looking at our scrapbook of madness."
a Paul McCartney
b George Harrison
c John Lennon

GROUP MEMBERS

Just one straight choice required here. A series of names - all you have to do is decide who they are called collectively.

QUESTION 1 *(5 POINTS)*
Dave Stewart, Peet Coombes, Annie Lennox, Jim Toomey, Eddie Chin

Q1
The writer in question?
b Richard Adams

QUESTION 2 *(5 POINTS)*
Richard Hell, Richard Lloyd, Tom Verlaine, Billy Ficca, Fred Smith

Q2
The movie soundtrack in question?
b Saturday Night Fever

QUESTION 3 *(5 POINTS)*
Paul Rodgers, Simon Kirke, Mick Ralphs, Boz Burrell

Q3
The cinematically-named artist?
a Harpo

QUESTION 4 *(6 POINTS)*
Ronnie Wood, Keith Richards, Stanley Clarke, Ian McLagan, Bobby Keys, Ziggy Modeliste

Q4
The composer in question?
a John Williams

QUESTION 5 *(4 POINTS)*
Archie, Reggie, Jughead, Betty, Veronica, Hot Dog

Q5
The fictitious rock star?
b Jim Maclaine

QUIZ 023 SEVENTIES POP GENIUS

THE PLACE TO BE

Five venue related questions.

Q1
Busy playing with his Action Man was
c Sid Vicious

Q2
The man with all that charisma?
a Freddie Mercury

Q3
Deliberating on unfaithfulness?
b John McVie

Q4
Gas, cigarettes and sunglasses?
b The Blues Brothers

Q5
Predicting the future was
c John Lennon

QUESTION 1 *(5 POINTS)*
In which town would you expect to find the legendary 70s prog rock venue Friars?
a Aylesbury
b Cheltenham
c Dunstable

QUESTION 2 *(5 POINTS)*
Which famous North London rock venue was grand enough to have a fish pond inside the foyer?
a The Marquee
b The Rainbow
c The 100 Club

QUESTION 3 *(5 POINTS)*
70s pub rock haven the Hope & Anchor is situated in which London borough?
a Kensington
b Islington
c Hackney

QUESTION 4 *(5 POINTS)*
Crosby, Stills, Nash and Young played the final concert of their marathon 1974 tour at which London venue?
a The Roundhouse
b Hyde Park
c Wembley Stadium

QUESTION 5 *(5 POINTS)*
The first Glastonbury festival held at Michael Eavis's Worthy Farm in 1970 saw which band headline?
a Fairport Convention
b The Kinks
c T. Rex

SEVENTIES POP GENIUS QUIZ 024

MR MOON

A true or false round in honour of The Who's late, great drummer and full-time comedian.

QUIZ 022

QUESTION 1 *(3 POINTS)*
Keith Moon was, with John Entwistle, jointly responsible for the naming of the quartet that became Led Zeppelin.
a True
b False

Q1
ANSWER
The Tourists

QUESTION 2 *(5 POINTS)*
Keith Moon's real name was Colin Smythe.
a True
b False

Q2
ANSWER
Television

QUESTION 3 *(6 POINTS)*
The title of the hyperactive drummer's one and only solo album was Moon The Loon.
a True
b False

Q3
ANSWER
Bad Company

QUESTION 4 *(5 POINTS)*
Keith Moon takes the lead vocal on 'Bell Boy' from The Who's album Quadrophenia.
a True
b False

Q4
ANSWER
The New Barbarians

QUESTION 5 *(6 POINTS)*
Moon died as a result of a sleeping pill overdose in 1974.
a True
b False

Q5
ANSWER
The Archies

29

QUIZ 023

METAL MASTERS

Five questions that any self-respecting heavy metal fan will have no difficulty with.

Q1

Friars is in
a Aylesbury

Q2

The grand venue
complete with
fish pond?
b The Rainbow

Q3

The Hope &
Anchor can be
found in the
borough of
b Islington

Q4

Crosby, Stills,
Nash and Young
played
c Wembley Stadium

Q5

The first
Glastonbury was
headlined by
c T. Rex

QUESTION 1 *(4 POINTS)*
Before Whitesnake, David Coverdale was a member of which of
these three bands?
a Deep Purple
b Black Sabbath
c Saxon

QUESTION 2 *(6 POINTS)*
What was the title of Iron Maiden's critically-praised debut EP
release launched the "New wave of British heavy metal"?
a 'The Soundhouse Tapes'
b 'Sounds Like New Metal'
c 'Live At The Prince Of Wales'

QUESTION 3 *(5 POINTS)*
The eponymously-titled Black Sabbath debut hit album was
released on which record label?
a Phillips
b Mercury
c Vertigo

QUESTION 4 *(5 POINTS)*
Judas Priest's 1978 album Stained Glass is illustrated by what
image on the cover?
a A shiny metallic head
b A stained glass cathedral window
c The band members pressing their faces against a shop window

QUESTION 5 *(5 POINTS)*
Name Eddie Van Halen's drummer brother in Van Halen.
a Peter Van Halen
b Willie Van Halen
c Alex Van Halen

CH, CH, CHANGES

David Bowie went through more changes in the 70s than most artists do in a life time. Five questions from Bowie's 70s timeline...

QUIZ 024

QUESTION 1 *(6 POINTS)*
On the single 'Fame', who shares a writing credit alongside long-time Bowie associate Carlos Alomar and Bowie himself?
a Marc Bolan
b John Lennon
c Mick Ronson

Q1
The Led Zeppelin naming was
a True

QUESTION 2 *(6 POINTS)*
What was the opening track on the Ziggy Stardust And The Spiders From Mars album?
a 'Five Years'
b 'Soul Love'
c 'Moonage Daydream'

Q2
Keith Moon's real name was Colin Smythe
b False. It was Keith Moon

QUESTION 3 *(4 POINTS)*
In which year did Bowie register his first British UK No.1 with 'Space Oddity'?
a 1971
b 1973
c 1975

Q3
Moon's solo album?
b False. Correct answer: Two Sides Of The Moon

QUESTION 4 *(5 POINTS)*
In the 70s movie The Man Who Fell To Earth, Bowie plays an alien visitor to earth. What was his character called?
a Carson
b Ziggy
c Newton

Q4
Keith Moon takes the lead vocal on 'Bell Boy'
a True

QUESTION 5 *(4 POINTS)*
Name Bowie's second British No.1 album, released in 1973.
a Aladdin Sane
b Diamond Dogs
c Pinups

Q5
b False. The overdose death took place in 1978

TRUE COLOURS

A set of teasing questions with five different colours at the heart of it...

Answers

QUIZ 025

Q1
Before Whitesnake, David Coverdale was a member of
a Deep Purple

Q2
Iron Maiden's debut EP was
a 'The Soundhouse Tapes'

Q3
The Black Sabbath debut hit album was released on
c Vertigo

Q4
Judas Priest's Stained Glass cover image?
a A shiny metallic head

Q5
Eddie Van Halen's drummer brother in Van Halen?
c Alex Van Halen

QUESTION 1 *(6 POINTS)*
Work out which of these three answers forms the second word in Al Green's second UK hit single?
a 'Love'
b 'Stay'
c 'Tired'

QUESTION 2 *(5 POINTS)*
Which duo recorded 'Blue Guitar' in 1975?
a Hall and Oates
b Justin Hayward and John Lodge
c Hudson-Ford

QUESTION 3 *(3 POINTS)*
What sort of night was it when Deep Purple went Top 2 in 1970?
a 'Black Night'
b 'White Night'
c 'Purple Night'

QUESTION 4 *(5 POINTS)*
'Black Betty' was a 1977 hit single for which of these acts?
a The Ramones
b Ram Jam
c Raydio

QUESTION 5 *(6 POINTS)*
Billy Ocean's 1977 No.2 hit includes one of these three traffic light colours, but which one?
a 'Red Light Spells Danger'
b 'Amber Light Means Caution'
c 'Go On The Green Light'

POP MATHEMATICS

A real brain bender with a correct number at the end of each of the five questions...

QUESTION 1 *(5 POINTS)*

Add the number of words in the title of Baccara's biggest hit single and subtract the number of No.1 hits The Who enjoyed in the 70s.

a 10
b 5
c 3

Q1
Sharing 'Fame'
writing credits
was
b John Lennon

QUESTION 2 *(5 POINTS)*

Add the peak chart place of 'You're The One That I Want' by John Travolta and Olivia Newton-John to the number of ELO's 'Overture' hit.

a 10927
b 10539
c 10001

Q2
The opening track
on Ziggy Stardust
And The Spiders
From Mars was
a Five Years

QUESTION 3 *(5 POINTS)*

Multiply Queen's number of 'Seas Of Rhye' by the number of steps to heaven in the Showaddywaddy hit.

a 33
b 18
c 21

Q3
Bowie's first
British UK No.1,
'Space Oddity',
was in
c 1975

QUESTION 4 *(5 POINTS)*

Take the number of 'Ways To Leave Your Lover' by Paul Simon and divide by the minutes in the title of The Stranglers' 1978 hit single.

a 10
b 25
c 5

Q4
Bowie's alien
visitor to earth
was
c Newton

QUESTION 5 *(5 POINTS)*

Subtract the number of 'Bars' in the 1976 Stylistics hit by the figure that begins the title of Amii Stewart's 1979 'Disco Heaven (Medley)'.

a 354
b 199
c 121

Q5
Bowie's second
British No.1
album was
c Pinups

LINE-UPS

Just one straight choice required here. A series of names - all you have to do is decide who they are called collectively…

QUESTION 1 *(7 POINTS)*
Sonja Kristina Linwood, Darryl Way, Francis Monkman, Florian Pilkington-Miksa

QUESTION 2 *(4 POINTS)*
Eric Clapton, Bobby Whitlock, Carl Radle, Jim Gordon, Duane Allman

QUESTION 3 *(3 POINTS)*
Dennis Locorriere, Ray Sawyer, George Cummings, Billy Francis

QUESTION 4 *(4 POINTS)*
Lou Gramm, Mick Jones, Ian McDonald, Ed Gagliardi, Dennis Elliott, Al Greenwood

QUESTION 5 *(7 POINTS)*
Maggie Bell, Les Harvey, James Dewar, John McGinnis, Colin Allen

QUIZ 027

Q1
'Let's Stay Together' was the Al Green hit title. So, the answer?
b 'Stay'

Q2
The duo in question was
b Justin Hayward and John Lodge

Q3
Deep Purple's night was
a 'Black Night'

Q4
'Black Betty' was a hit for
b Ram Jam

Q5
Billy Ocean's 1977 hit was
a 'Red Light Spells Danger'

PARTNERSHIPS

Who featured with who on some of the 70s biggest hits.

QUIZ 028

QUESTION 1 *(7 POINTS)*

Who featured with Johnny Mathis on his 1978 hit 'Too Much, Too Little, Too Late'?

a Gladys Knight
b Deniece Williams
c Natalie Cole

QUESTION 2 *(2 POINTS)*

Who joined Elton John on the chart-topper 'Don't Go Breaking My Heart'?

a Kiki Dee
b Tina Turner
c Millie Jackson

QUESTION 3 *(6 POINTS)*

Who sang vocals on Led Zeppelin's album track 'The Battle Of Evermore'?

a Mary Hopkin
b Sally Oldfield
c Sandy Denny

QUESTION 4 *(5 POINTS)*

Who was the contributor to the Diana Ross single 'Stop Look Listen (To Your Heart)?

a Marvin Gaye
b Michael Jackson
c Smokey Robinson

QUESTION 5 *(5 POINTS)*

Who joined forces with Barbra Streisand on her US million-selling single 'You Don't Bring Me Flowers'?

a Barry Gibb
b Robin Gibb
c Neil Diamond

Q1
'Yes Sir, I Can Boogie' minus the number of Who No.1s =
b 5

Q2
Chart position 1 + '10538 Overture' =
b 10539

Q3
'Seven Seas of Rhye' x 'Three Steps To Heaven' =
c 21

Q4
50 ways divided by '5 Minutes' =
a 10

Q5
'Sixteen Bars' subtracted from '137 Disco Heaven' =
c 121

QUIZ 031 SEVENTIES POP GENIUS

FIVE GO DANCING

Dance related questions for the decade that brought you disco. Every 70s song answer here begins with the word 'Dancing'.

QUIZ 029

Q1
ANSWER
Curved Air

Q2
ANSWER
Derek and the Dominos

Q3
ANSWER
Dr. Hook

Q4
ANSWER
Foreigner

Q5
ANSWER
Stone The Crows

QUESTION 1 *(5 POINTS)*
Which of these did their 'Dancing With The Captain'?
a Captain And Tennille
b Pluto Shervington
c Paul Nicholas

QUESTION 2 *(5 POINTS)*
Which of these did their 'Dancin' In The Moonlight'?
a Thin Lizzy
b Tina Charles
c Sad Café

QUESTION 3 *(5 POINTS)*
Which of these did their 'Dancing On A Saturday Night'?
a Christie
b Barry Blue
c Billy Swan

QUESTION 4 *(5 POINTS)*
Which of these did their 'Dancing In The City'?
a Marshall Hain
b Manhattan Transfer
c Leif Garrett

QUESTION 5 *(5 POINTS)*
Which of these enjoyed a 'Dancin' Party'?
a The Rubettes
b Showaddywaddy
c Paul Nicholas

TOP OF THE POPS

The BBC flagship pop show proved to make or break an act in the 70s.
Five questions all related to the acts and the presenters.

QUIZ 030

QUESTION 1 *(7 POINTS)*
Only one act had the presence of mind to name a record after the decade's greatest pop show and register a hit; who were they?
a The Rezillos
b Buzzcocks
c Sham 69

QUESTION 2 *(4 POINTS)*
Which of these dance groups never appeared on Top Of The Pops?
a Hot Gossip
b Legs & Co
c Pan's People

QUESTION 3 *(6 POINTS)*
Who was Top Of The Pops' first producer, in charge until leaving the show in 1973?
a Mike Mansfield
b Johnnie Stewart
c David Jacobs

QUESTION 4 *(4 POINTS)*
Which of these three Top Of The Pops presenters was the only one to actually front the programme in the 1970s?
a Ed Stewart
b Andy Peebles
c Mike Smith

QUESTION 5 *(4 POINTS)*
In which year did David Bowie give his legendary Top Of The Pops performance of 'Starman'?
a 1971
b 1972
c 1973

Q1
Featured on the Johnny Mathis hit was
b Deniece Williams

Q2
Joined Elton John on 'Don't Go Breaking My Heart'?
a Kiki Dee

Q3
Vocals on Led Zeppelin's 'The Battle Of Evermore'?
c Sandy Denny

Q4
Contributing to 'Stop Look Listen (To Your Heart)?
a Marvin Gaye

Q5
Joining forces with Barbra Streisand was
c Neil Diamond

37

QUIZ 033 SEVENTIES POP GENIUS

QUIZ 031

ALBUM CHART-TOPPERS

An assortment of questions based around the biggest hitting albums of the decade...

Q1
'Dancing With The Captain'?
c Paul Nicholas

Q2
'Dancin' In The Moonlight'?
a Thin Lizzy

Q3
'Dancing On A Saturday Night'?
b Barry Blue

Q4
'Dancing In The City'?
a Marshall Hain

Q5
Enjoying a 'Dancin' Party'?
b Showaddywaddy

QUESTION 1 *(3 POINTS)*
Bread's one and only No.1 LP was called what?
a The Smell Of Bread
b The Sound Of Bread
c The Loaf Of Bread

QUESTION 2 *(5 POINTS)*
All with their own particular merits, but which of these three releases failed to make No.1 in the album chart?
a The Dark Side Of The Moon by Pink Floyd
b Red River Valley by Slim Whitman
c In Through The Out Door by Led Zeppelin

QUESTION 3 *(6 POINTS)*
Status Quo registered a hat-trick of No.1 albums in the 70s. First came Hello in 1973, then On The Level in 1975. What came third in 1976?
a Piledriver
b If You Can't Stand The Heat
c Blue For You

QUESTION 4 *(5 POINTS)*
Cosmo's Factory was the title of the No.1 album by which North American act?
a Jefferson Starship
b The Allman Brothers
c Creedence Clearwater Revival

QUESTION 5 *(6 POINTS)*
Which of these three Rolling Stones No.1 albums included the tracks 'Angie', 'Star Star' and 'Silver Train'?
a Exile On Main St
b Goat's Head Soup
c Get Yer Ya-Ya's Out!

SPOT THE YEAR

Three singles, three years. Choose the correct one…

QUESTION 1 *(5 POINTS)*

In which year did 'I Saw The Light' by Todd Rundgren, 'Snoopy Versus The Red Baron' by The Hotshots and 'Gaudete' by Steeleye Span chart?

a 1971
b 1973
c 1975

QUESTION 2 *(5 POINTS)*

'Silver Lady' by David Soul,' Egyptian Reggae' by Jonathan Richman & The Modern Lovers and '2-4-6-8 Motorway' by Tom Robinson: which year?

a 1977
b 1978
c 1979

QUESTION 3 *(5 POINTS)*

'Cool For Cats' by Squeeze, 'Pop Muzik' by M and 'Silly Games' by Janet Kay: which year?

a 1977
b 1978
c 1979

QUESTION 4 *(5 POINTS)*

'A Horse With No Name' by America, 'Meet Me On The Corner' by Lindisfarne and 'Family Affair' by Sly And The Family Stone: which year?

a 1970
b 1971
c 1972

QUESTION 5 *(5 POINTS)*

'Jeans On' by David Dundas, 'Mississippi' by Pussycat and 'Substitute' by The Who: which year?

a 1975
b 1976
c 1977

SLADE: LOOK WOT WE'VE DUN!

Five questions all about the boys from the black country...

Q1
Bread's one and only No.1 LP was called
b The Sound Of Bread

Q2
Failed to make No.1 in the chart?
a The Dark Side Of The Moon by Pink Floyd

Q3
Status Quo's third chart-topping album?
c Blue For You

Q4
Cosmo's Factory was by
c Creedence Clearwater Revival

Q5
The Stones No.1 album in question was
b Goat's Head Soup

QUESTION 1 *(4 POINTS)*
Who was the band's drummer?
a Jim Lea
b Don Powell
c Dave Hill

QUESTION 2 *(6 POINTS)*
In the group's mid-70s movie Flame, which character did lead vocalist Noddy Holder play?
a Stoker
b Charlie
c Basher

QUESTION 3 *(5 POINTS)*
In their early incarnation before the glam rock years, Slade dressed in the style of which of these youth tribes?
a Teddy boys
b Hippies
c Skinheads

QUESTION 4 *(5 POINTS)*
Which name and birth place correctly identifies Noddy Holder?
a Norman Holder: born West Bromwich
b Neville Holder: born Walsall
c Nigel Holder: born Wednesbury

QUESTION 5 *(5 POINTS)*
What was Slade's first hit single?
a 'Coz I Luv You'
b 'Get Down And Get With It'
c 'My Friend Stan'

SEVENTIES POP GENIUS QUIZ 034

AWOL IN THE DECADE

Maybe they were too early or maybe they were too late. This is a round devoted to well-known artists for whom the 70s were a barren decade with no chart action...

QUIZ 034

QUESTION 1 *(5 POINTS)*
Which of these three star names failed to record a single hit in the 70s?
a Percy Sledge
b Joe Cocker
c Average White Band

QUESTION 2 *(5 POINTS)*
Which is the no-show from these three?
a Charles Aznavour
b Randy Crawford
c The Four Tops

QUESTION 3 *(5 POINTS)*
Which is the no-show from these three?
a Hawkwind
b Kraftwerk
c Louis Armstrong

QUESTION 4 *(5 POINTS)*
Which is the no-show from these three?
a Graham Parker and The Rumour
b Tom Petty and The Heartbreakers
c Prince

QUESTION 5 *(5 POINTS)*
Which is the no-show from these three?
a The Skids
b Ray Charles
c UB40

Q1
The year in question?
b 1973

Q2
'2-4-6-8 Motorway', 'Egyptian Reggae' and 'Silver Lady'?
a 1977

Q3
'Cool For Cats', 'Pop Muzik' and 'Silly Games' all hit big in
c 1979

Q4
All three hits were from
c 1972

Q5
'Jeans On', 'Mississippi' and 'Substitute' all appeared in
b 1976

41

QUIZ 037 SEVENTIES POP GENIUS

QUIZ 035

Q1
Slade's drummer?
b Don Powell

Q2
The Flame movie character Noddy played was
a Stoker

Q3
Fashionably, Slade were
c Skinheads

Q4
Noddy is
b Neville Holder: born Walsall

Q5
Slade's first hit single?
b 'Get Down And Get With It'

WHISTLE TEST TEST

The BBC's Old Grey Whistle Test was the no frills rock antidote to Top Of The Pops. Five questions on the show filmed in what appeared to be nothing more than a store cupboard…

QUESTION 1 *(5 POINTS)*
Select the correct date for the first screening of the show.
a 21st September 1971
b 1st October 1972
c 12th November 1973

QUESTION 2 *(5 POINTS)*
Which of these three OGWT presenters hosted the very first show?
a Richard Williams
b Mark Ellen
c Bob Harris

QUESTION 3 *(5 POINTS)*
Which band were responsible for the programme's harmonica-driven theme tune 'Stone Fox Chase'.
a Manfred Mann
b Area Code 615
c Ducks Deluxe

QUESTION 4 *(5 POINTS)*
In 2001, OGWT's longest-serving presenter, Bob Harris, published his autobiography. What was the title?
a The Whispering Years
b A Life Spent Whispering
c Whispering Tales

QUESTION 5 *(5 POINTS)*
Select the closest figure that describes the number of editions of the programme until its demise in the 80s?
a 500
b 1000
c 2000

WHO ARE YOU?
Get the answers from the three clues in each of the five questions…

QUIZ 038

QUESTION 1 *(4 POINTS)*
'Showdown', 'Shine A Little Love' and 'Telephone Line' were all 70s hits for which act?
a The Fall
b Electric Light Orchestra
c The Glitter Band

QUESTION 2 *(5 POINTS)*
This solo artist was born in Ontario, Canada, and had six UK chart entries including albums Don Quixote and Sundown.
a Neil Young
b Joni Mitchell
c Gordon Lightfoot

QUESTION 3 *(6 POINTS)*
A Song For Me, Anyway and Fearless were three of this act's five 70s hit albums.
a Cliff Richard
b Crosby, Stills And Nash
c Family

QUESTION 4 *(6 POINTS)*
John Kay was guitarist and vocalist; they had literally a Monster of an album which topped the US chart; they were formed in Los Angeles.
a Buffalo Springfield
b Steppenwolf
c Love

QUESTION 5 *(4 POINTS)*
Reportedly Prince Charles's favourite group, they had their first hit, 'Year Of Decision', and their biggest, 'When Will I See You Again', in 1974.
a The Stylistics
b The Three Degrees
c The Chi-Lites

Q1
Failing to record a single hit in the 70s?
a Percy Sledge

Q2
The no-show?
b Randy Crawford

Q3
Absent without leave in the 70s?
c Louis Armstrong

Q4
Not a single hit?
c Prince

Q5
A barren decade was had by
b Ray Charles

QUIZ 039 SEVENTIES POP GENIUS

THE BOYS AND GIRLS IN THE BAND

Decide who these people are called collectively…

Q1
The first Whistle Test?
a 21st September 1971

Q2
First OGWT presenter?
a Richard Williams

Q3
The harmonica-driven theme tune was by
b Area Code 615

Q4
The Bob Harris autobiography?
a The Whispering Years

Q5
The number of editions of the programme?
a 500

QUESTION 1 *(3 POINTS)*
Leslie McKeown, Stuart 'Woody' Wood, Eric Faulkner, Alan Longmuir, Derek Longmuir

QUESTION 2 *(6 POINTS)*
Howard Devoto, John McGeoch, Barry Adamson, Martin Jackson, Dave Formula

QUESTION 3 *(5 POINTS)*
Steve Winwood, Dave Mason, Chris Wood, Jim Capaldi

QUESTION 4 *(5 POINTS)*
Joan Jett, Cherie Currie, Lita Ford, Jackie Fox, Sandy West

QUESTION 5 *(6 POINTS)*
Elkie Brooks, Robert Palmer, Conrad Isidore, Tim Hinkley, Steve York, Pete Gage

SEVENTIES POP GENIUS  QUIZ 040

PICTURED ON THE SLEEVE

Five album covers you need to conjure up in your mind's eye…

QUESTION 1 *(5 POINTS)*
The fox illustrated on the front cover of the Genesis album Foxtrot is wearing what?
a A white swim suit
b A black top hat
c A red evening dress

QUESTION 2 *(5 POINTS)*
Which Fleetwood Mac LP sleeve features a dog attacking some unfortunate person's leg?
a Rumours
b Tusk
c Greatest Hits

QUESTION 3 *(5 POINTS)*
The Jethro Tull cover for Thick As A Brick is in the form of a newspaper front page. What is the title of the newspaper?
a The St. Neots News and Biggleswade Examiner
b The St. Cleve Chronicle and Linwell Advertiser
c The St. Boswell Telegraph and Border Times

QUESTION 4 *(5 POINTS)*
Which of artist Roger Dean's 1970s fantasy album covers features a flying elephant?
a Topographic Oceans by Yes
b Osibisa by Osibisa
c Demons And Wizards by Uriah Heep

QUESTION 5 *(5 POINTS)*
What creature adorns the front cover of Nazareth's 1973 Top 10 album Loud 'N' Proud?
a Eagle owl
b Lion
c Peacock

Q1
All three hits were by
b Electric Light Orchestra

Q2
The Canadian vocalist / instrumentalist is
c Gordon Lightfoot

Q3
All albums by
c Family

Q4
The question's factual clues all point to
b Steppenwolf

Q5
Reportedly honoured with royal approval?
b The Three Degrees

45

DAZED AND CONFUSED

Hopefully you will be by the time you have finished this Led Zeppelin quiz…

Q1
THE LINE-UP
ANSWER
Bay City Rollers

Q2
THE LINE-UP
ANSWER
Magazine

Q3
THE LINE-UP
ANSWER
Traffic

Q4
THE LINE-UP
ANSWER
The Runaways

Q5
THE LINE-UP
ANSWER
Vinegar Joe

QUESTION 1 *(3 POINTS)*
Which Led Zeppelin track was hi-jacked by the BBC for the Top Of The Pops theme tune?
a 'Whole Lotta Love'
b 'Kashmir'
c 'When The Levee Breaks'

QUESTION 2 *(8 POINTS)*
Legend has it that at the height of their popularity, the band's John Paul Jones was close to leaving for which reason?
a To circumnavigate the globe in a balloon
b To train to be an airline pilot
c To become a cathedral choirmaster

QUESTION 3 *(5 POINTS)*
In 1974, the band launched their own record label called what?
a Unicorn Records
b Swan Song Records
c Led Zeppelin Records

QUESTION 4 *(5 POINTS)*
At which venue did Zeppelin break the box office and attendance records set by The Beatles a decade earlier at Shea Stadium?
a Madison Square Garden, New York
b Tampa Stadium, Florida
c Candlestick Park, San Francisco, California

QUESTION 5 *(4 POINTS)*
Which Led Zeppelin album includes the epic 10-minute 25-second-long track 'Achilles Last Stand'?
a Physical Graffiti
b Presence
c The Song Remains The Same

THE KATE BUSH TEST

Test your knowledge of Britain's first woman to top the UK album chart...

QUESTION 1 *(5 POINTS)*

Where was Kate Bush born?

a Cambridge, Cambridgeshire
b Guildford, Surrey
c Bexleyheath, Kent

Q1
**The Genesis fox
is wearing**
c A red evening
dress

QUESTION 2 *(4 POINTS)*

**Which music legend insisted EMI listen to her songs, thereby
creating the fact that he 'discovered' Kate?**

a George Martin
b Dave Gilmour
c George Harrison

Q2
**The Fleetwood
Mac LP is**
b Tusk

QUESTION 3 *(5 POINTS)*

In which year did Kate hit the road for her first and last tour?
a 1977
b 1978
c 1979

Q3
**The Jethro Tull
newspaper?**
b The St. Cleve
Chronicle and
Linwell Advertiser

QUESTION 4 *(6 POINTS)*

**What was the name given to the UK and European tour
mentioned in question 3?**

a Tour Of Life
b Song And Dance Tour
c Full House Tour

Q4
**Roger Dean's
flying elephant
features on**
b Osibisa by
Osibisa

QUESTION 5 *(5 POINTS)*

**Which single included: "He'll never make the screen,. He'll never make
the Sweeney. Bet that movie queen, he's too busy hitting the Vaseline."**

a 'The Man With The Child In His Eyes'
b 'Wow'
c 'Wuthering Heights'

Q5
**The Nazareth
cover creature is**
c Peacock

QUIZ 043 SEVENTIES POP GENIUS

THE NAME'S BOND

We stray into a little movie know-how with these five questions about Britain's favourite spy…

QUESTION 1 *(4 POINTS)*
The 'Live And Let Die' theme tune came courtesy of Wings, but which actor played Bond in the movie?
a George Lazenby
b Timothy Dalton
c Roger Moore

QUESTION 2 *(5 POINTS)*
Carly Simon was responsible for which one of these three Bond themes?
a 'The Spy Who Loved Me'
b 'The Man With The Golden Gun'
c 'Moonraker'

QUESTION 3 *(6 POINTS)*
Bond tune 'Diamonds Are Forever' became something of a signature piece for Shirley Bassey. Which position did the record reach in 1972?
a 13
b 38
c 2

QUESTION 4 *(6 POINTS)*
Only one of these three acts recorded a 70s Bond theme…
a Lulu
b Dionne Warwick
c Sheena Easton

QUESTION 5 *(4 POINTS)*
All-time record-breaker: which of these three composers has written the most Bond themes?
a John Barry
b Marvin Hamlisch
c Don Black

SEVENTIES POP GENIUS QUIZ 044

COME TOGETHER

Just one straight choice required here. A series of names - all you have to do is decide who they are when they come together...

QUESTION 1 *(5 POINTS)*
Marcia Barrett, Maizie Williams, Liz Mitchell, Bobby Farrell

Q1
Where was Kate Bush born?
c Bexleyheath, Kent

QUESTION 2 *(5 POINTS)*
Thijs Van Leer, Jan Akkerman, Bert Ruiter, Pierre Van Der Linden

Q2
Kate's champion was
b Dave Gilmour

QUESTION 3 *(5 POINTS)*
Robert Wyatt, Kevin Ayers, Mike Ratledge

Q3
Kate's first and last tour was in
c 1979

QUESTION 4 *(5 POINTS)*
Russell Mael and Ron Mael

Q4
The name of the tour?
a Tour Of Life

QUESTION 5 *(5 POINTS)*
Maddy Prior, Tim Hart, Bob Johnson, Rick Kemp, Peter Knight

Q5
The single in question was
b 'Wow'

BLUE IS THE COLOUR

"Blue is the colour, football is the game" sang the Chelsea footballers, but this quiz is more about the state of mind than winning the FA Cup…

QUIZ 043

Q1

The 'Live And Let Die' Bond was
c Roger Moore

Q2

Carly Simon was responsible for
a 'The Spy Who Loved Me'

Q3

The chart peak reached by 'Diamonds Are Forever'?
b 38

Q4

The act in question was
a Lulu

Q5

The composer who has written the most Bond themes?
a John Barry

QUESTION 1 *(5 POINTS)*
Who registered their 18th Top 10 album with the release of Black And Blue in 1976?
a Status Quo
b The Rolling Stones
c Diana Ross

QUESTION 2 *(5 POINTS)*
Identify the biggest hit single taken from Elton John's Blue Moves album. Only one of these actually appeared on the 1976 release.
a 'Song For Guy'
b 'Sorry Seems To Be The Hardest Word'
c 'Part Time Love'

QUESTION 3 *(5 POINTS)*
Who went Top 3 with their two biggest hits, 'Banner Man' and 'Melting Pot'?
a The Moody Blues
b Blue Mink
c The Blues Band

QUESTION 4 *(5 POINTS)*
Linda Ronstadt had a US million-seller and her second modest UK chart hit with this song…
a 'Blue Water'
b 'Blue Bayou'
c 'Blue Velvet'

QUESTION 5 *(5 POINTS)*
Blues guitarist Gary Moore had his first solo hit single at the close of the decade. Name that tune…
a 'Parisienne Walkways'
b 'Out In The Fields'
c 'Because Of Your Love'

IN BRACKETS

Here's some well-known songs to find with only the bracketed bit at the end of the title to work with…

QUESTION 1 *(6 POINTS)*

What's the main title that precedes '(Yowsah Yowsah)'?

a 'Car Wash' by Rose Royce
b 'Dance Dance Dance' by Chic
c 'Stool Pigeon' by Kid Creole And The Coconuts

Q1
The line-up in question?
Boney M

QUESTION 2 *(4 POINTS)*

Find the front half of '(Blow Your Mind This Time)'.

a 'Fire' by The Pointer Sisters
b 'Didn't I' by The Delfonics
c 'Can You Feel The Force' by The Real Thing

Q2
The line-up in question?
Focus

QUESTION 3 *(5 POINTS)*

This T. Rex hit from 1973 strangely ends '(Tyke)'.

a 'Jeepster'
b 'The Groover'
c 'Truck On'

Q3
The line-up in question?
Soft Machine

QUESTION 4 *(5 POINTS)*

Which of these three is the correct choice to begin a hit that ended '(The First Time)'?

a 'Loving And Free' by Kiki Dee
b 'Summer' by Bobby Goldsboro
c 'Zing Went The Strings Of My Heart' by The Trammps

Q4
The duo in question?
Sparks

QUESTION 5 *(5 POINTS)*

Which of these hits ends with '(On The Bayou)'?

a 'Jambalaya' by the Carpenters
b 'Green River' by Creedence Clearwater Revival
c 'Spiders And Snakes' by Jim Stafford

Q5
The line-up in question?
Steeleye Span

QUIZ 045

A MERRY HIT-MAKING CHRISTMAS

Five festive brainteasers…

Q1
Black And Blue in 1976? It was
b The Rolling Stones

Q2
The Blue Moves hit was
b 'Sorry Seems To Be The Hardest Word'

Q3
'Banner Man' and 'Melting Pot' were by
b Blue Mink

Q4
Linda Ronstadt had a US million-seller with
b Blue Bayou

Q5
Gary Moore's first solo hit?
a 'Parisienne Walkways'

QUESTION 1 *(5 POINTS)*
A hit decades earlier in the US, Bing Crosby's 'White Christmas' failed to chart in the UK until 1977. Who wrote the world's best-seller?
a Bing Crosby
b Irving Berlin
c Johnny Mercer

QUESTION 2 *(4 POINTS)*
'You Ain't Seen Nothing Yet', 'Lonely This Christmas' and 'Juke Box Jive' made up the Christmas week top three in which year?
a 1974
b 1975
c 1976

QUESTION 3 *(6 POINTS)*
Slade's seasonal stomper 'Merry Xmas Everybody' was actually recorded in a summer heatwave, but where?
a London
b Berlin
c New York

QUESTION 4 *(5 POINTS)*
When Queen made Christmas No.1 in 1975 with the single 'Bohemian Rhapsody', they also topped the album chart with which LP?
a A Night At The Opera
b A Day At The Races
c Sheer Heart Attack

QUESTION 5 *(5 POINTS)*
Who had a Top 20 hit in 1974 with the simply-titled 'Christmas Song'?
a Donny Osmond
b Gilbert O'Sullivan
c Greg Lake

POP ANATOMY

A set of questions dedicated to parts of the human body…

QUIZ 048

QUESTION 1 *(3 POINTS)*
What sort of 'Legs' did Rod Stewart sing about in 1978?
a 'Hot Legs'
b 'Long Legs'
c 'Sexy Legs'

QUESTION 2 *(5 POINTS)*
Which is the correct title of American band Little Feat's late 70s album?
a Feets Don't Fail Me Now
b Heart Don't Fail Me Now
c Legs Don't Fail Me Now

QUESTION 3 *(4 POINTS)*
Who had a hit titled 'Back Stabbers' in 1972?
a The Stylistics
b Curtis Mayfield
c The O'Jays

QUESTION 4 *(6 POINTS)*
'Fat Bottomed Girls' appeared as one half of Queen's double A-side single in 1978: what was the other half?
a 'Don't Stop Me Now'
b 'Save Me'
c 'Bicycle Race'

QUESTION 5 *(7 POINTS)*
Des O'Connor had eight Top 30 singles, beginning with 'Careless Hands' in 1967, but what was the title of his biggest 70s hit?
a 'You Need Hands'
b 'The Tip Of My Fingers'
c 'Under My Thumb'

Q1
Ahead of '(Yowsah Yowsah)'?
b 'Dance Dance Dance' by Chic

Q2
The front half of '(Blow Your Mind This Time)'?
b 'Didn't I' by The Delfonics

Q3
The hit strangely ending '(Tyke)'?
c 'Truck On'

Q4
The front bit of '(The First Time)'?
b 'Summer' by Bobby Goldsboro

Q5
The hit that ends with '(On The Bayou)'?
a 'Jambalaya' by the Carpenters

53

BORN IN THE USA

An all-American quiz featuring some classic pop and rock acts that made a big impression in 70s Britain and some who clearly didn't...

Q1

The 'White Christmas' song-writer?
b Irving Berlin

Q2

All three Christmas hits charted in
a 1974

Q3

'Merry Xmas Everybody' was recorded in
c New York

Q4

The LP involved in Queen's double?
a A Night At The Opera

Q5

The 'Christmas Song' was a hit for
b Gilbert O'Sullivan

QUESTION 1 *(4 POINTS)*
Which female solo artist followed up her early 70s hit 'Both Sides Now' with the 67-week chart limpet 'Amazing Grace'?
a Joan Baez
b Judy Collins
c Joni Mitchell

QUESTION 2 *(7 POINTS)*
What was unusual about The Detroit Emeralds' 'Feel The Need In Me'?
a They released the same song via two different recordings and had two hits with it. **b** The song was actually written by members of The Detroit Spinners but didn't chart for them. **c** The single spent more weeks at No.2 in the UK chart without hitting the top spot than any other single during the 70s.

QUESTION 3 *(6 POINTS)*
Which of these 70s Top 10 US chart act names is completely made up?
a Daddy Dewdrop
b Steve Dahl and Teenage Radiation
c Dalai Larma

QUESTION 4 *(4 POINTS)*
Which of these three Ray Stevens singles gave him his only UK No.1?
a 'The Streak'
b 'Misty'
c 'Bridget The Midget'

QUESTION 5 *(4 POINTS)*
Which state gave birth to Bob Dylan?
a Minnesota
b New Hampshire
c North Carolina

SEVENTIES POP GENIUS QUIZ 050

ALL ABOUT FREDDIE

Five right royal questions dedicated to Queen frontman Freddie Mercury...

QUESTION 1 *(5 POINTS)*

In which year was Faroukh Bulsara, as he was then named, born?

a 1939

b 1943

c 1946

QUESTION 2 *(5 POINTS)*

A Freddie Mercury statue by Czech sculptor Irena Sedlecka is situated in which of these European cities?

a Barcelona

b Montreux

c Athens

QUESTION 3 *(5 POINTS)*

Freddie played in a number of groups before Queen. Which of these three is the band that wasn't graced with his presence?

a Smile

b Ibex

c Sour Milk

QUESTION 4 *(5 POINTS)*

In which year did Queen attract 150,000 fans to a free concert in Hyde Park, London?

a 1976

b 1977

c 1978

QUESTION 5 *(5 POINTS)*

In 1979, Freddie performed with one of these British institutions. Pick the correct association.

a The Royal Scots Dragoon Guards

b The Royal Ballet

c Dame Vera Lynn

Q1
Rod Stewart's legs in 1978 were
a 'Hot Legs'

Q2
The correct Little Feat album title?
a Feets Don't Fail Me Now

Q3
'Back Stabbers' was a hit for
c The O'Jays

Q4
The 'other' A-Side in question?
c 'Bicycle Race'

Q5
Des O'Connor's biggest 70s hit?
b 'The Tip Of My Fingers'

QUIZ 049

RADIO ONE-DERFUL

BBC's Radio 1 gets the question and answer treatment...

Q1
The female solo artist in question?
b Judy Collins

Q2
The unusual fact?
a Same song via two different recordings and had two hits with it

Q3
The fictitious act?
c Dalai Larma

Q4
Ray Stevens's only UK No.1 was
a 'The Streak'

Q5
Bob Dylan's state of birth?
a Minnesota

QUESTION 1 *(4 POINTS)*
The Radio 1 Breakfast Show was anchored by just three presenters during the 70s. Tony Blackburn, Noel Edmonds and who?
a Mike Smith
b Mike Read
c Dave Lee Travis

QUESTION 2 *(4 POINTS)*
Which Radio 1 DJ was most associated with the often tear-jerking feature Our Tune?
a Simon Bates
b Alan Freeman
c Bruno Brookes

QUESTION 3 *(6 POINTS)*
Chart act Laurie Lingo And The Dipsticks were better known as which DJ duo?
a Dave Lee Travis and Paul Burnett
b Peter Powell and Mike Read
c John Peel and David Jensen

QUESTION 4 *(6 POINTS)*
Which trumpeter in the Alan Price Set was producer to broadcasting legend John Peel and also best man at his wedding?
a Derek Chinnery
b John Walters
c Paul Gambaccini

QUESTION 5 *(5 POINTS)*
Unsurprisingly, Emperor Rosko was not the great DJ's real name. Which of these three names ring true?
a Wayne Zalewski
b Hugh Grant
c Mike Pasternak

PINK FLOYDTASTIC

One of British music's greatest treasures: five questions most Pink Floyd fans will have no problems with…

QUESTION 1 *(5 POINTS)*
Where does the Pink Floyd band name come from?
a US bluesmen Pink Anderson and Floyd Council
b Roger Waters's pet rat Pink and Rick Wright's boxer dog Floyd
c After the bank robber Pretty Boy Floyd, immortalised in the Woody Guthrie song of the same name.

Q1
Freddie Mercury, then Faroukh Bulsara, was born in
c 1946

QUESTION 2 *(5 POINTS)*
In which city were the band formed?
a Oxford
b Cambridge
c Bath

Q2
The Freddie statue is situated in
b Montreux

QUESTION 3 *(5 POINTS)*
Name the band's drummer.
a Richard Wright
b Nick Mason
c Syd Barrett

Q3
The band not graced with Freddie's presence?
a Smile

QUESTION 4 *(5 POINTS)*
What animal appears on the cover of the Pink Floyd LP Atom Heart Mother?
a A flying pig
b A cow in a field
c A hen surrounded by her brood of chicks

Q4
Queen's free concert in Hyde Park, London, was in
a 1976

QUESTION 5 *(5 POINTS)*
What was the title of the Pink Floyd album that featured a picture of London's Battersea Power Station on the cover?
a Wish You Were Here
b Meddle
c Animals

Q5
In 1979, Freddie performed with
b The Royal Ballet

MILLION-SELLERS

All five of the following questions are loosely based on British hit singles that sold more than one million copies.

QUIZ 051

Q1
The DJ in question was
c Dave Lee Travis

Q2
The Our Tune DJ was
a Simon Bates

Q3
The hit duo was
a Dave Lee Travis and Paul Burnett

Q4
The best man, trumpeter and producer?
b John Walters

Q5
Emperor Rosko was
c Mike Pasternak

QUESTION 1 *(7 POINTS)*
'Save Your Kisses For Me' gave Brotherhood Of Man a million-selling single and which other pop achievement in 1976?
a It broke the points record at the Eurovision Song Contest
b They became the first UK group to register a No.1 single in the 70s
c The release became the best-selling record in the USA in 1976

QUESTION 2 *(4 POINTS)*
David Soul had a million-seller with 'Don't Give Up On Us'. Which character did he play in the TV series Starsky and Hutch?
a David Starsky
b Ken Hutchinson
c Huggy Bear

QUESTION 3 *(5 POINTS)*
Which of these three classic hits failed to shift a million back in the 70s?
a 'Dancing Queen' by Abba
b 'Y.M.C.A.' by The Village People
c 'Summer Nights' by John Travolta and Olivia Newton-John

QUESTION 4 *(4 POINTS)*
The Boney M million-seller 'Rivers Of Babylon' was a double A-side single backed by which of these?
a 'Mary's Boy Child'
b 'Ma Baker'
c 'Brown Girl In The Ring'

QUESTION 5 *(5 POINTS)*
Away from the 70s for a moment – how many single releases do you think have passed the million mark since the chart began in 1952?
a Just under 100
b Just under 500
c Just under 2000

THE YEAR IN QUESTION IS 1972

1972 is the year. How much do you remember?

`QUIZ 052`

QUESTION 1 *(4 POINTS)*
Which UK group had a hit with 'Part Of The Union'?
a Jethro Tull
b Fleetwood Mac
c The Strawbs

QUESTION 2 *(6 POINTS)*
Which of these three was not a hit for Elton John in 1972?
a 'Rocket Man'
b 'Crocodile Rock'
c 'Your Song'

QUESTION 3 *(5 POINTS)*
Around this time the band called Hotlegs change their name to what?
a Roxy Music
b Lieutenant Pigeon
c 10cc

QUESTION 4 *(4 POINTS)*
Which legendary musician in his mid 50s had a bizarre No.1 with 'My Ding-A-Ling' in 1972?
a Bing Crosby
b George Benson
c Chuck Berry

QUESTION 5 *(6 POINTS)*
A year of novelty hits saw which of these singles top the chart at Christmas?
a 'Grandad' by Clive Dunn
b 'Ernie (The Fastest Milkman In The West)' by Benny Hill
c 'Long Haired Lover From Liverpool' by Little Jimmy Osmond

Q1
Pink Floyd were
a Named after US bluesmen Pink Anderson and Floyd Council

Q2
The city in which the band were formed?
b Cambridge

Q3
The band's drummer?
a Richard Wright

Q4
The animal pictured on the cover of Atom Heart Mother?
b A cow in a field

Q5
The Battersea Power Station album title?
c Animals

QUIZ 053

ELVIS: 70s SUPERSTAR

The decade was incredibly successful for 'The King', who statistically spent more weeks on the singles chart and had more hits than any other act…

Q1

The answer?
a It broke the points record at the Eurovision Song Contest

Q2

David Soul played
b Ken Hutchinson

Q3

The classic in question was
a 'Dancing Queen' by Abba

Q4

'Rivers Of Babylon' was backed by
c 'Brown Girl In The Ring'

Q5

The number of million-sellers?
a Just under 100

QUESTION 1 *(6 POINTS)*
Elvis enjoyed two UK No.1 hit singles in the 70s. 'Way Down' was the second, but what was the first?
a 'Burning Love'
b 'I Just Can't Help Believing'
c 'The Wonder Of You'

QUESTION 2 *(4 POINTS)*
When Presley died, who was the then US President who said: "Elvis Presley's death deprives our country of a part of itself"?
a Gerald Ford
b Jimmy Carter
c Ronald Reagan

QUESTION 3 *(4 POINTS)*
In which US state will you find Elvis's Graceland home?
a Tennessee
b Mississippi
c Alabama

QUESTION 4 *(7 POINTS)*
What was significant about a concert in Phoenix, Arizona, in August 1970?
a It was the last live performance before his death
b It was the start point of his first US tour since the 1950s
c It was cancelled due to a heavy snow fall

QUESTION 5 *(4 POINTS)*
As a mark of respect after his death, Elvis's record company re-issued his singles. Name the record label.
a Columbia
b Atlantic
c RCA

PUT THEM TOGETHER
WHAT HAVE YOU GOT?
Five more groups to identify.

QUESTION 1 *(4 POINTS)*
Errol Brown, Harvey Hinsley, Patrick Olive, Tony Connor, Larry Ferguson

Q1
The UK group responsible for 'Part Of The Union'?
c The Strawbs

QUESTION 2 *(6 POINTS)*
Alan Hull, Ray Jackson, Rod Clements, Ray Laidlaw

Q2
The Elton John song that was not a hit in 1972?
c 'Your Song'

QUESTION 3 *(4 POINTS)*
Les Gray, Rob Davis, Ray Stiles, Dave Mount

Q3
Hotlegs changed their name to
c 10cc

QUESTION 4 *(6 POINTS)*
Stuart Adamson, William Simpson, Thomas Kellichan, Richard Jobson

Q4
The musician that charted with 'My Ding-A-Ling' was
c Chuck Berry

QUESTION 5 *(5 POINTS)*
Graham Gouldman, Eric Stewart, Lol Crème, Kevin Godley

Q5
The Christmas No.1 in question?
c 'Long Haired Lover From Liverpool' by Little Jimmy Osmond

QUIZ 055

WHAT'S MISSING?

Each of these five 70s tracks include a gap you need to fill. Select the correct word to complete the song titles...

Q1
The first of two Elvis No.1s in the 70s?
c 'The Wonder Of You'

Q2
The US President in question?
b Jimmy Carter

Q3
Graceland is in the state of
a Tennessee

Q4
The significant Elvis concert?
b The start point of his first US tour since the 1950s

Q5
The record label in question?
c RCA

QUESTION 1 *(5 POINTS)*
Mick Jagger's '_____ From Turner'
a 'Letter'
b 'Memo'
c 'Love'

QUESTION 2 *(5 POINTS)*
Led Zeppelin's '_____ Dog'
a 'Black'
b 'Good'
c 'Sheep'

QUESTION 3 *(5 POINTS)*
Leo Sayer's 'Long _____ Glasses'
a 'Short'
b 'Tall'
c 'Cool'

QUESTION 4 *(5 POINTS)*
Lobo's 'Me And You And A _____ Named Boo'
a 'Cat'
b 'Dog'
c 'Girl'

QUESTION 5 *(5 POINTS)*
Pink Floyd's 'Careful With That _____, Eugene'
a 'Axe'
b 'Knife'
c 'Gun'

FIGURE THESE OUT

The number is the answer in these five brain-teasers...

QUESTION 1 *(4 POINTS)*
How many volts in the name of this group who charted with 'I'm On Fire' and 'Doctor Kiss-Kiss'?
a 500 Volts
b 5000 Volts
c 10000 Volts

Q1
The group?
Hot Chocolate

QUESTION 2 *(6 POINTS)*
King Cotton was a Top 10 album for this 70s outfit, but can you 'piece' together their group name?
a One Penny Piece
b Five Penny Piece
c Ten Penny Piece

Q2
This quartet is
Lindisfarne

QUESTION 3 *(4 POINTS)*
Which is the correct address in the title of this 1973 Gene Pitney hit?
a '18 Sycamore'
b '24 Sycamore'
c '64 Sycamore'

Q3
Les Gray and co were
Mud

QUESTION 4 *(4 POINTS)*
What lengths did T. Rex go to in their 1972 Top 10 hit?
a 'One Inch Rock'
b 'Ten Inch Rock'
c 'Ninety Inch Rock'

Q4
The band in question?
The Skids

QUESTION 5 *(7 POINTS)*
The Keef Hartley Band's 1972 album featured a picture of a native American Indian on the cover, but what was the LP title?
a Seventy-Second Brave
b Thirty-Third Chief
c Fifty-Ninth Redskin

Q5
This quartet add up to
Hotlegs /10cc

QUIZ 057

PICK A YEAR

Struggle with dates? This quiz gives a double helping hand by nominating the No.1 album and No.1 single in a particular week to help you pinpoint the correct year...

Q1
Mick Jagger's
'_____ From
Turner'
b 'Memo'

QUESTION 1 *(5 POINTS)*
Let It Be (The Beatles) and 'Back Home' (England World Cup Squad) were No.1 in May of which year?
a 1970
b 1971
c 1972

Q2
Led Zeppelin's
'_____ Dog'
a 'Black'

QUESTION 2 *(5 POINTS)*
Reggatta De Blanc (The Police) and 'One Day At A Time' (Lena Martell) were No.1 in October of which year?
a 1977
b 1978
c 1979

Q3
Leo Sayer's
'Long _____
Glasses,
b 'Tall'

QUESTION 3 *(5 POINTS)*
Atlantic Crossing (Rod Stewart) and 'Hold Me Close' (David Essex) were No.1 in October of which year?
a 1973
b 1974
c 1975

Q4
Lobo's 'Me And
You And A _____
Named Boo'
b 'Dog'

QUESTION 4 *(5 POINTS)*
We All Had Doctors' Papers (Max Boyce) and 'Space Oddity'(David Bowie) were No.1 in November of which year?
a 1973
b 1974
c 1975

Q5
Pink Floyd's
'Careful With
That _____,
Eugene'
a 'Axe'

QUESTION 5 *(5 POINTS)*
Ooh La La (The Faces) and 'Tie A Yellow Ribbon Round The Ole Oak Tree' (Dawn) were No.1 in April of which year?
a 1972
b 1973
c 1974

LYRICALLY SPEAKING

Five precious points for every song correctly identified…

QUESTION 1 *(5 POINTS)*

"Don't go changing, to try and please me. You never let me down before."

QUESTION 2 *(5 POINTS)*

"Throw me a line I'm sinking fast. Clutching at straws can't make it."

QUESTION 3 *(5 POINTS)*

"You're my sun, my moon, my guiding star. My kind of wonderful, that's what you are."

QUESTION 4 *(5 POINTS)*

"Redcoats in the village and there's fighting in the streets. The Indians and the mountain men, well they are talking when they meet."

QUESTION 5 *(5 POINTS)*

"The road is long, with many a winding turn. That leads us to who knows where."

QUIZ 061 SEVENTIES POP GENIUS

THE ONE AND ONLY

One 70s hit single and nothing more is what links these five questions...

Q1
Let It Be and 'Back Home' were both No.1 in
a 1970

Q2
Reggatta De Blanc and 'One Day At A Time' topped charts in
c 1979

Q3
Atlantic Crossing and 'Hold Me Close' were chart-toppers in
c 1975

Q4
We All Had Doctors' Papers and 'Space Oddity', No.1 in
c 1975

Q5
Ooh La La and 'Tie A Yellow Ribbon..." hit No.1 in,
b 1973

QUESTION 1 *(4 POINTS)*
Who became a one-hit wonder with 'My Resistance Is Low' in 1976?
a Peter Sarstedt
b Robin Sarstedt
c Barry Sarstedt

QUESTION 2 *(7 POINTS)*
Which French outfit went Top 10 and then disappeared with 'Pepper Box'?
a The Peppers
b Salt and Pepper
c The Salt Sisters

QUESTION 3 *(4 POINTS)*
'Midnight At The Oasis' was this act's only UK chart visit.
a Ann Peebles
b Minnie Riperton
c Maria Muldaur

QUESTION 4 *(4 POINTS)*
Just once did this solo artist trouble the singles chart. The release that did it for him was 'Rio'.
a Michael Nesmith
b Peter Tork
c Micky Dolenz

QUESTION 5 *(6 POINTS)*
The distinctive hit 'I Get A Kick Out Of You' was on the chart for eight weeks in 1974. Select the correct male vocalist.
a Richard Stilgoe
b Mike Batt
c Gary Shearston

ALL YOU NEED IS LOVE

"Cupid, draw back your bow" (as Sam Cooke once sang) and find the answer to these five questions of love…

QUIZ 060

QUESTION 1 *(5 POINTS)*
'Loop Di Love' was a smash hit for which of these romantic acts?
a Love Unlimited
b Shag
c Bill Lovelady

QUESTION 2 *(5 POINTS)*
Name the act responsible for 'Love's Gotta Hold On Me'.
a Dollar
b Bucks Fizz
c Billy Ocean

QUESTION 3 *(4 POINTS)*
'Love Is Like Oxygen' for which of these three?
a Roxy Music
b The Sweet
c Malcolm Roberts

QUESTION 4 *(6 POINTS)*
The novelty song 'Loving You Has Made Me Bananas' was the work of which of these solo artists in 1978?
a Guy Marks
b Dean Friedman
c Mark Lovelace

QUESTION 5 *(5 POINTS)*
'Float On' by The Floaters introduces the band members and their star signs. It begins "Aquarius, and my name is…" Name that Floater.
a Larry
b Ralph
c James

Q1
This love lyric line?
'Just The Way You Are' by Billy Joel

Q2
These words come from
'Virginia Plain' by Roxy Music

Q3
The love song is
'You're The First, The Last, My Everything' by Barry White

Q4
These lines?
'The Boston Tea Party' by The Sensational Alex Harvey Band

Q5
The directions come from
'He Ain't Heavy, He's My Brother' The Hollies

HEAVY QUESTIONING

A set of questions about some of rock's heaviest acts…

Q1

'My Resistance Is Low' was by
b Robin Sarstedt

QUESTION 1 *(5 POINTS)*
Name the band who were album chart mainstays in the 70s with titles like Return To Fantasy, Demons And Wizards and Sweet Freedom.
a Saxon **b** Uriah Heep **c** Hawkwind

Q2

The French outfit in question?
a The Peppers

QUESTION 2 *(5 POINTS)*
AC/DC lead vocalist Bon Scott emigrated to Australia aged six from where?
a Gateshead, England
b Kirriemuir, Scotland
c Cork, Republic Of Ireland

Q3

'Midnight At The Oasis' was the only UK chart visit for
c Maria Muldaur

QUESTION 3 *(5 POINTS)*
Who had a Top 10 hit in 1979 with 'Since You've Been Gone'?
a Whitesnake
b Thin Lizzy
c Rainbow

Q4

The solo artist who went to 'Rio'?
a Michael Nesmith

QUESTION 4 *(5 POINTS)*
Originally written by Kansas Joe McCoy and Memphis Minnie, it's the final song on Led Zeppelin's fourth album. Name that track.
a 'When The Levee Breaks'
b 'Stairway To Heaven'
c 'Misty Mountain Hop'

Q5

The correct male vocalist?
c Gary Shearston

QUESTION 5 *(5 POINTS)*
In which year did Tarkus by Emerson, Lake And Palmer top the UK album chart?
a 1970
b 1971
c 1972

SEVENTIES POP GENIUS  QUIZ 064

ONE-WORD ANSWERS

Five questions with just one word required for each answer.

QUESTION 1 *(5 POINTS)*
American group The Moments And The Whatnauts had a one-word hit with all shapes and sizes of what in 1975?

'Loop Di Love' was a smash hit for
b Shag

QUESTION 2 *(5 POINTS)*
Four letters, one word: it's the title for a No.2 hit by Tom Jones in 1971 that we're after.

'

The act responsible for 'Love's Gotta Hold On Me'?
a Dollar

QUESTION 3 *(4 POINTS)*
The Kinks sang about a couple of different girls in 1970. This one, according to the lyrics, was the result of a meeting in a Soho bar.

'Love Is Like Oxygen' was a hit for?
b The Sweet

QUESTION 4 *(6 POINTS)*
Having already eliminated one name in question 3, who was the other girl that was the subject of a 1970 Kinks hit?

The novelty song solo artist in question was
a Guy Marks

QUESTION 5 *(5 POINTS)*
The first Tubeway Army album was called what?

The Floater was
b Ralph

PICTURE THIS

A picture quiz to tax your powers of observation, with five points for each correct identification.

Q1
The band name?
b Uriah Heep

QUESTION 1 *(5 POINTS)*
Who's the blonde?

Q2
Bon Scott emigrated to Australia from?
b Kirriemuir, Scotland

QUESTION 2 *(5 POINTS)*
Name the album cover on which this gentleman appears.

Q3
The band responsible for 'Since You've Been Gone'?
c Rainbow

QUESTION 3 *(5 POINTS)*
Five whole points just for the name of the singer in this cropped image.

Q4
The final song on Led Zeppelin's fourth album?
a 'When The Levee Breaks'

QUESTION 4 *(5 POINTS)*
Identify this chart-topping LP and the group responsible.

Q5
Tarkus topped the UK chart in?
b 1971

QUESTION 5 *(5 POINTS)*
Name the band and the album title inspired by this Imperial War Museum image.

SEVENTIES POP GENIUS ▌QUIZ 066

CHART-TOPPING LYRICS

A lyrics round involving five 70s No.1 singles. You will need the song and the artist to take maximum points.

QUESTION 1 *(4 POINTS)*
Which 1974 chart-topper included the lines: "Well, he says he's into his music but I don't believe him. He just doesn't seem to understand the rock media."

Q1
The one word hit was all shapes and sizes of
'Girls'

QUESTION 2 *(4 POINTS)*
Identify this No.1 from 1970: "If her daddy's rich, take her out for a meal. If her daddy's poor, just do what you feel."

Q2
The No.2 hit by Tom Jones?
'Till'

QUESTION 3 *(4 POINTS)*
These are the opening two lines to the best-selling hit in August 1979. "The silicone chip inside her head gets switched to overdrive."

Q3
The girl in the Kinks hit song?
'Lola'

QUESTION 4 *(5 POINTS)*
"Ladies and gentlemen, this is captain Tobias Wilcock welcoming you aboard Coconut Airways Flight 372 to Bridgetown, Barbados." 1975 was the year: who was the artist and what was the song?

Q4
The 'other' Kinks girl was
'Victoria'

QUESTION 5 *(8 POINTS)*
Identify the song and the artist from the closing lines from this 1974 chart-topper: "It is just my jealous mind. It's in love that I'm so blind. Blame it on my jealous mind. So forgive my jealous mind."

Q5
The first Tubeway Army album?
'Replicas'

71

ISLAND RECORDS

All answers in this quiz share a common thread. Every question answered successfully reveals a well-known act who was signed to the much-loved Island label.

Q1

The blonde?
Rick Wakeman

QUESTION 1 *(4 POINTS)*
'Lady D'Arbanville' and 'Another Saturday Night' were hit singles for Island, sung by who?

Q2
The gent appears on the cover of
Ooh La La by The Faces

QUESTION 2 *(7 POINTS)*
Handsworth Revolution was one of many key album releases by the label. Identify the group behind the record, named after the area in Birmingham they sprang from.

Q3

The image is of
Donna Summer

QUESTION 3 *(5 POINTS)*
Who is the legendary founder of Island Records?

Q4
The group and album?
Every Good Boy Deserves Favour by The Moody Blues

QUESTION 4 *(5 POINTS)*
Fire And Water and Free At Last were just two albums from this Island act.

Q5
The band and the album title?
Setting Sons by The Jam

QUESTION 5 *(4 POINTS)*
Natty Dread was the first album to chart for which Island reggae group?

SEVENTIES POP GENIUS QUIZ 068

MATCH UP
Select the correct act to match up with each of these 70s record releases.

QUESTION 1 *(4 POINTS)*
Which of these three acts took 'Hello Happiness' to No.12 in the UK singles chart?
a The Drifters
b The Stylistics
c The Four Tops

Q1
The chart-topper in question?
'Gonna Make You A Star' by David Essex

QUESTION 2 *(6 POINTS)*
Who had a Top 30 hit with 'Smokin' In The Boys' Room' in 1974?
a J Geils Band
b Brownsville Station
c Blackfoot Sue

Q2
The1970 summer anthem? '
In The Summertime' by Mungo Jerry

QUESTION 3 *(5 POINTS)*
'The Rubberband Man' was a 1976 Top 20 chart hit for who?
a The Bellamy Brothers
b The Doobie Brothers
c The Detroit Spinners

Q3
The opening two lines?
'I Don't Like Mondays' by The Boomtown Rats

QUESTION 4 *(5 POINTS)*
Who was the 'Rochdale Cowboy' in 1975?
a Joe Jackson
b Mike Harding
c Andy Fairweather-Low

Q4
The song and act in question?
'Barbados' by Typically Tropical

QUESTION 5 *(5 POINTS)*
Who took 'Yellow River' to the top of the singles chart in 1970?
a Jimmy Osmond
b Gary Puckett And The Union Gap
c Christie

Q5
The Identity of the song and the artist...
'Jealous Mind' by Alvin Stardust

IDENTITY PARADE

There's no margin for error here. You need every member of each band to gain maximum points.

QUIZ 067

Q1
Both songs were sung by
Cat Stevens

QUESTION 1 *(4 POINTS)*
Name the five Rolling Stones band members at the time of their Exile On Main St (1972) album recordings. Five points only if you get all five.

Q2
The Brummie band in question?
Steel Pulse

QUESTION 2 *(4 POINTS)*
Name all three in The Jam's line-up.

Q3
The Island Records founder?
Chris Blackwell

QUESTION 3 *(4 POINTS)*
All four members of The Clash responsible for the Give 'Em Enough Rope (1978) album gets you five points.

Q4
The Island act was
Free

QUESTION 4 *(6 POINTS)*
The quartet credited with Genesis' seventh studio album A Trick Of The Tail (1976). Six points only if you can name all four of the band.

Q5
Natty Dread was the first hit album by
Bob Marley and The Wailers

QUESTION 5 *(7 POINTS)*
Another seven points are yours for the full group line-up that recorded The Rise And Fall Of Ziggy Stardust And The Spiders From Mars (1972).

LONDON CALLING

Five questions linked only by references to the capital city.

QUIZ 068

QUESTION 1 *(2 POINTS)*

What do Sherlock Holmes and Gerry Rafferty have in common?

Q1
**'Hello Happiness'
was a hit for**
a The Drifters

QUESTION 2 *(7 POINTS)*

Which tube station is the title of a song linking Jimi Hendrix and Rod Stewart?

Q2
**'Smokin' In The
Boys' Room' was
by**
b Brownsville
Station

QUESTION 3 *(5 POINTS)*

On which Clash album did the track 'London Calling' first appear?

Q3
**'The Rubberband
Man' came
courtesy of**
c The Detroit
Spinners

QUESTION 4 *(6 POINTS)*

The 100 Club was (and still is) situated in which London street?

Q4
**The 'Rochdale
Cowboy'?**
b Mike Harding

QUESTION 5 *(5 POINTS)*

Crosby, Stills, Nash & Young played an outdoor concert in the capital in 1974. What was the venue?

Q5
**'Yellow River'
topped the
singles chart for**
c Christie

QUIZ 071 SEVENTIES POP GENIUS

SEX SELLS
Sex certainly sells product and the record industry is no exception.

QUESTION 1 *(6 POINTS)*
'Sexy Cream' was a modest hit for which of these 70s groups?
a The Slits
b Sex Pistols
c Slick

QUESTION 2 *(4 POINTS)*
Hot Chocolate's 'You Sexy Thing' went Top 10 in which year?
a 1971
b 1973
c 1975

QUESTION 3 *(5 POINTS)*
**Which is the correct full title of James Brown's classic track
'Sex Machine'?**
a '(I Feel Like A) Sex Machine'
b 'Get Up (I Feel Like Being A) Sex Machine'
c 'Get On Up (I'm A) Sex Machine'

QUESTION 4 *(4 POINTS)*
**Sex was the name of the kinky fashion boutique responsible for
launching the Sex Pistols. Name the duo that ran the shop.**
a Simon Dee and Richard Hell
b David Bowie and Twiggy
c Malcolm McLaren and Vivienne Westwood

QUESTION 5 *(6 POINTS)*
**Disco Tex & The Sex-O-Lettes had two hits in the mid-70s. Which
of these three was not a hit for US act fronted by Sir Monti Rock III?**
a 'Get Dancing'
b 'I Wanna Dance Wit Choo (Doo Dat Dance) – Part 1'
c 'Dancin' Kid'

JOB DONE

A bit of hard graft never hurt anyone. Here's a quiz hanging loosely on the 9-5 peg.

QUIZ 070

QUESTION 1 *(3 POINTS)*

Not just a working relationship. Which is the correct description linking Carpenters Karen and Richard?

a Brother and sister
b Husband and wife
c Cousins

Q1
Answer '
Baker Street' was
home to Sherlock
and it was Gerry's
biggest hit

QUESTION 2 *(6 POINTS)*

In which year was The Grateful Dead's Workingman's Dead recorded and released?

a 1970
b 1971
c 1972

Q2
Answer
'Angel' is the
station (and song
written by Jimi and
recorded by Rod)

QUESTION 3 *(4 POINTS)*

"Meet the new boss. Same as the old boss" was a line from which Who track?

a 'Won't Get Fooled Again'
b 'Relay'
c '5:15'

Q3
Answer
'London Calling'
appeared on the
album London
Calling

QUESTION 4 *(6 POINTS)*

The other half of the partnership (a group manager and sometime actor) who with Tony Wilson founded and ran Factory Records?

a Rob Gretton
b Alan Erasmus
c Martin Hannet

Q4
**The location of
the 100 Club...**
Oxford Street

QUESTION 5 *(6 POINTS)*

Alan Price's 1974 hit 'Jarrow Song' is the tale of a miner who marches to London for work. Which is the correct start to the song?

a "My name is Georgie Wilkinson..."
b "My name is Geordie McIntyre..."
c "My name is Jarrow McIlroy..."

Q5
**The CSN&Y
venue?**
Wembley Stadium

77

GONNA MAKE YOU A STAR

Not all these stars shone that brightly but each is still worth five points.

QUIZ 071

Q1
'Sexy Cream'
was a hit for
c Slick

Q2
Hot Chocolate's
'You Sexy Thing'
went Top 10 in
c 1975

Q3
James Brown's
classic in full?
b 'Get Up (I Feel
Like Being A) Sex
Machine'

Q4
The duo?
c Malcolm McLaren
and Vivienne
Westwood

Q5
The non-Sex-o-
Lettes hit?
c 'Dancin' Kid'

QUESTION 1 *(5 POINTS)*
Ringo Starr managed a string of four Top 10 hits in the 70s, but what was the former Beatle's 'real' name?
a Richard Starkey
b Rory Storm
c Roy Williams

QUESTION 2 *(5 POINTS)*
Edwin Starr followed up his 70s smash hit 'War' with two more Top 10 singles. Which of these three didn't make the Top 10?
a 'Stop The War Now'
b 'Contact'
c 'H.A.P.P.Y. Radio'

QUESTION 3 *(5 POINTS)*
Which of these three 'stars' had a Top 10 hit with 'It's You'?
a Alvin Stardust
b Twinkle
c Freddie Starr

QUESTION 4 *(5 POINTS)*
When The Buggles released 'Video Killed The Radio Star' they were a duo. Who was Trevor Horn's keyboard-playing partner?
a Nick Kershaw
b Geoff Downes
c Chris Spedding

QUESTION 5 *(5 POINTS)*
Stevie Wonder's 1976 album Songs In The Key Of Life contained a starry track title. Pick the right star.
a 'Paradise Star'
b 'Another Star'
c 'The Wrong Star'

FANCY THAT

Five questions odd enough to prompt a surprise response.

QUESTION 1 *(4 POINTS)*

Williams is the commonest name in pop. Which of the nine 70s hit-makers with that name topped the singles chart with 'Free'?

a Deniece Williams

b Danny Williams

c John Williams

Q1

The correct relationship?

a Brother and sister

QUESTION 2 *(6 POINTS)*

With so many artists named Williams here's another on the topic. Which of these stars had a 1976 hit with 'I Recall A Gypsy Woman'?

a Andy Williams

b Iris Williams

c Don Williams

Q2

Workingman's Dead was recorded and released in

a 1970

QUESTION 3 *(6 POINTS)*

It's one of the shortest titled hits of the 70s: who released 'D.J.'?

a David Bowie

b Genesis

c George Harrison

Q3

"Meet the new boss. Same as the old boss"?

a 'Won't Get Fooled Again'

QUESTION 4 *(4 POINTS)*

Amazingly, Elton John had no No.1 singles in the 70s as a solo artist. Which of his 24 attempts came closest?

a 'Song For Guy'

b 'Daniel'

c 'Rocket Man (I Think It's Going To Be A Long Long Time)'

Q4

The other half of the partnership?

b Alan Erasmus

QUESTION 5 *(5 POINTS)*

Concluding the 'fancy that' theme, which of these 70s acts charted with 'Fancy Pants'?

a Black Lace

b Kenny

c The Rubettes

Q5

The 'Jarrow Song' opening?

b "My name is Geordie McIntyre..."

MONEY, MONEY, MONEY

Hard cash, cheques, credit cards: all are accepted here for the next five questions.

Answers

QUIZ 073

Q1
Ringo's 'real' name?
a Richard Starkey

Q2
Edwin Starr's follow-up flop was
a 'Stop The War Now'

Q3
'It's You'? It's
c Freddie Starr

Q4
Trevor Horn's partner?
b Geoff Downes

Q5
The right star?
b 'Another Star'

QUESTION 1 *(4 POINTS)*
Dollar duo David Van Day and Thereze Bazar formally comprised one-third of which group?
a Bucks Fizz
b Guys 'n' Dolls
c Brotherhood Of Man

QUESTION 2 *(7 POINTS)*
'Money, Money, Money' by Abba broke a sequence of three No.1s. What was the single's peak position?
a No.3
b No.9
c No.14

QUESTION 3 *(5 POINTS)*
Released in 1979, 'Brass In Pocket' by The Pretenders featured band member Chrissie Hynde playing what role in the song's video?
a Airline pilot
b City banker
c Café waitress

QUESTION 4 *(4 POINTS)*
In which year did The Flying Lizards hit the Top 5 with 'Money'?
a 1975
b 1977
c 1979

QUESTION 5 *(5 POINTS)*
What warning or advice do Pink Floyd give in the lyrics to the song 'Money', immediately after the words "Share it fairly..."
a "Share it fairly and try to get high"
b "Share it fairly but don't take a slice of my pie"
c "Share it fairly - don't ask the question why"

ALL IN A YEAR
Three fantastic hits listed for each year. Name the year.

QUIZ 074

QUESTION 1 *(5 POINTS)*
In which year did 'Mittageisen (Metal Postcard)' by Siouxsie & The Banshees, 'Morning Dance' by Spyro Gyra and 'Walking On The Moon' by The Police all first hit the chart?

a 1977 **b** 1978 **c** 1979

Q1
Which Williams topped the chart with 'Free'?
a Deniece Williams

QUESTION 2 *(5 POINTS)*
Fireball by Deep Purple, Fearless by Family and Surf's Up by The Beach Boys: three classic albums that all entered the chart for the first time in which year?

a 1970 **b** 1971 **c** 1972

Q2
Who recalled a gypsy woman?
c Don Williams

QUESTION 3 *(5 POINTS)*
'Tragedy' by the Bee Gees, 'Sarah' by Thin Lizzy and 'Luton Airport' by Cats U.K. all entered the chart when?

a 1975 **b** 1977 **c** 1979

Q3
'D.J.' was by
a David Bowie

QUESTION 4 *(5 POINTS)*
In which year did 'The Trail Of The Lonesome Pine' by Laurel and Hardy, 'Life Is A Minestrone' by 10cc and 'Boogie On Reggae Woman' by Stevie Wonder all grace the singles chart?

a 1975 **b** 1976 **c** 1977

Q4
Elton's closest?
c 'Rocket Man
(I** Think It's Going To Be A Long Long Time)'

QUESTION 5 *(5 POINTS)*
'S-S-S-Single Bed' by Fox, 'Little Does She Know' by the Kursaal Flyers and 'Play That Funky Music' by Wild Cherry were all hits in which year?

a 1976 **b** 1977 **c** 1978

Q5
The 'Fancy Pants' act?
b Kenny

81

QUIZ 075

ROCK ANAGRAMS

With a clue in each case to get you started, re-arrange the letters to spell a well-known 70s rock or pop act...

Q1

The group in question?

b Guys 'n' Dolls

QUESTION 1 *(3 POINTS)*

Three words required for three easy points if you want to go all the way.

THE HOT TOP MOLE

Q2

Peak position for 'Money, Money, Money'?

a No.3

QUESTION 2 *(6 POINTS)*

Make two words to spell the name of a punk leader.

CANNABIS EPISTLE

Q3

Chrissie Hynde played a...

c Café waitress

QUESTION 3 *(5 POINTS)*

Create two-words to spell out these folk.

TEN EL PEAS YES

Q4

The Flying Lizards hit the Top 5 with 'Money' in

c 1979

QUESTION 4 *(5 POINTS)*

Re-arrange these ten letters to form a two word Welsh band name.

CRANE OR MEN

Q5

Pink Floyd's advice is

b "Share it fairly but don't take a slice of my pie"

QUESTION 5 *(6 POINTS)*

This variously-named outfit are ready for lift-off if you can put all these letters in the correct order and make two words.

JASPER FRONT FISHES

82

SEVENTIES POP GENIUS QUIZ 078

GIRL POWER

Five questions surrounding five of the decade's finest female solo artists.

QUIZ 078

QUESTION 1 *(6 POINTS)*
'Raised On Robbery', 'Free Man In Paris' and 'Help Me' were three of the tracks from which Joni Mitchell album?
a The Hissing Of Summer Lawns
b Court And Spark
c Ladies Of The Canyon

Q1
The year in question?
c 1979

QUESTION 2 *(5 POINTS)*
Patti Smith's 1978 Top 20 album was called what?
a Easter
b Christmas
c Thanksgiving

Q2
All three entered the chart in
b 1971

QUESTION 3 *(5 POINTS)*
How many British hit singles did Tina Turner enjoy as a solo performer in the 70s?
a None
b Seven
c 21

Q3
Three hits, one year...
c 1979

QUESTION 4 *(5 POINTS)*
Which one of these three 70s LP releases by Dusty Springfield failed to chart in the UK?
a From Dusty… With Love
b It Begins Again
c Dusty In Memphis

Q4
The year in question?
a 1975

QUESTION 5 *(4 POINTS)*
In which US state was Dolly Parton born?
a South Carolina
b Tennessee
c Kentucky

Q5
This trio of hits all happened in
b 1977

83

LOVE LYRICS

Five more questions for the lyrically inclined with love on their mind.
As before, you must supply both the artist and the song to take all the
available points.

QUIZ 077

Q1
**The required
three words?**
Mott The Hoople

QUESTION 1 *(6 POINTS)*
**Name this love song from 1975. "Aggravated – spare for days. I
troll downtown the red light place. Jump up bubble up – what's
in store..."**

Q2
The punk leader?
Captain Sensible

QUESTION 2 *(5 POINTS)*
**This song was just pipped to the No.1 spot in 1976: "You run
around town like a fool and you think that it's groovy. You're
giving it to some other guy who gives you the eye."**

Q3
**The folk in
question?**
Steeleye Span

QUESTION 3 *(4 POINTS)*
**Artist and song required for all the points. "All of you brothers
over in Africa. Tell all the folks in Egypt and Israel too. Please
don't miss this train at the station."**

Q4
**The Welsh band
name?**
Amen Corner

QUESTION 4 *(4 POINTS)*
**What 1973 Top 10 hit is this? "And when you go away. I know
my heart can stay with my love, it's understood. It's in the hands
of my love and my love does it good."**

Q5
**The band ready
for lift-off?**
Jefferson Starship

QUESTION 5 *(6 POINTS)*
**A 1971 hit for a US solo artist. Recognise this? "When you're
down and confused. And you don't remember who you're talkin'
to. Concentration - slip away. Coz your baby is so far away."**

SEVENTIES POP GENIUS  QUIZ 080

DIFFERENT SONGS SAME TITLE

Questions about five different 70s hit songs that share the same title..

QUIZ 078

QUESTION 1 *(7 POINTS)*
Both Eric Clapton and Buzzcocks had minor hits with two different songs that shared the same title. Name the song.
a 'I Don't Mind'
b 'Promises'
c 'Love You More'

QUESTION 2 *(4 POINTS)*
Which shared different song with the same title do Elton John and Gladys Knight and The Pips have in common?
a 'Part Time Love'
b 'Philadelphia Freedom'
c 'Crazy Water'

QUESTION 3 *(5 POINTS)*
Different songs, same titles: the acts this time are David Essex and Simon & Garfunkel.
a 'Lamplight'
b 'Coming Home'
c 'America'

QUESTION 4 *(4 POINTS)*
Roxy Music and The Crusaders are linked by which of these smash hits?
a 'Dance Away'
b 'All I Want Is You'
c 'Street Life'

QUESTION 5 *(5 POINTS)*
The Rubettes and The Move share different hits with which title?
a 'Chinatown'
b 'Tonight'
c 'California Man'

Q1
The Joni
Mitchell album in
question?
b Court And Spark

Q2
Patti Smith's
1978 Top 20
album was
a Easter

Q3
The number
of British hit
singles Tina
Turner enjoyed?
a None

Q4
The Dusty chart
failure?
c Dusty In Memphis

Q5
Dolly's state of
birth?
b Tennessee

85

QUIZ 079

QUIZ 081 SEVENTIES POP GENIUS

TOUGH AND EASY

Five tough questions based on the 70s' top easy listening performers.

Q1

The love song in question?
'Love Is The Drug' by Roxy Music

Q2

The song pipped for the top spot?
'Love Really Hurts Without You' by Billy Ocean

Q3

The artist and song?
'Love Train' by The O'Jays

Q4

The 1973 Top 10 hit was
'My Love' by Paul McCartney and Wings

Q5

The song and US solo artist?
'Love The One You're With' by Stephen Stills

QUESTION 1 *(5 POINTS)*
'Solitaire' provided Andy Williams with a Top 4 chart position in 1973, but which duo wrote the song?
a Nicky Chinn and Mike Chapman
b Carole King and Carole Bayer Sager
c Neil Sedaka and Phil Cody

QUESTION 2 *(6 POINTS)*
UK vocalist Tony Christie's real name is what?
a Chris Teesdale
b Francis Christie
c Tony Fitzgerald

QUESTION 3 *(4 POINTS)*
Al Martino will go down in history as the first artist to be No.1 in the UK's first pop chart in 1952. What was the crooner's only 70s hit?
a 'Spanish Fly'
b 'Spanish Eyes'
c 'Spanish Woman'

QUESTION 4 *(6 POINTS)*
How many hit albums did Frank Sinatra rack up in the 70s?
a None
b Six
c 12

QUESTION 5 *(4 POINTS)*
Which well known actress was Burt Bacharach married to throughout the 70s?
a Angie Dickenson
b Goldie Hawn
c Farrah Fawcett

DID I REALLY SAY THAT?

Five quotes with five rock and pop legends to match them to. No options to choose from, but the answers should be as straight forward as they come.

QUESTION 1 *(5 POINTS)*
Who bragged: "When I first knew Elvis, he had a million dollars worth of talent. Now he has a million dollars."

QUESTION 2 *(5 POINTS)*
Which lady said: "I wasn't born with a wig and make-up."

QUESTION 3 *(5 POINTS)*
Can you guess who would be most likely to have admitted: "Convicts are the best audiences I ever played for."

QUESTION 4 *(5 POINTS)*
Who predictably boasted that "It doesn't matter that I carry a gun, or have bodyguards, or live in a fortified mansion. When I go into a recording studio, I make art."

QUESTION 5 *(5 POINTS)*
Who joked: "As far as I'm concerned, the benefit of being a black Irishman is that I pull more chicks."

QUIZ 081

QUIZ 083 SEVENTIES POP GENIUS

HERE COMES THE SUN

Let the sun shine in and 25 points could be yours.

Q1
The writing duo were
a Nicky Chinn and Mike Chapman

QUESTION 1 *(5 POINTS)*
Who had a Top 20 hit with 'Sunshine Day' in 1976?
a Steel Pulse
b Ashford and Simpson
c Osibisa

Q2
Tony Christie's real name?
c Tony Fitzgerald

QUESTION 2 *(4 POINTS)*
Which group went Top 5 with 'Summer Night City'?
a Abba
b The Beach Boys
c The Isley Brothers

Q3
Al Martino's only 70s UK hit?
b 'Spanish Eyes'

QUESTION 3 *(7 POINTS)*
Who suffered from 'Sunburn' in 1979?
a Mike Batt
b Graham Gouldman
c Bay City Rollers

Q4
The number of hit albums racked up by Frank Sinatra?
c Twelve

QUESTION 4 *(4 POINTS)*
Who had a Top 10 hit single in 1977 with 'Sunshine After The Rain'?
a Gloria Gaynor
b Elkie Brooks
c Meri Wilson

Q5
Burt Bacharach was married to
a Angie Dickenson

QUESTION 5 *(5 POINTS)*
'Summer (The First Time)' was a hit for which North American singer?
a Terry Jacks
b Bobby Goldsboro
c Andrew Gold

THE JACKSONS

A round devoted to five questions about the Jackson family.

QUESTION 1 *(5 POINTS)*

The Jackson Five's first UK hit entered the chart in January 1970. Name that debut hit single.

a 'ABC'
b 'Lookin' Through The Windows'
c 'I Want You Back'

Q1
The million-dollar quote was from
Colonel Tom Parker

QUESTION 2 *(6 POINTS)*

Who wrote and also recorded the Jackson Five's 1973 hit 'Doctor My Eyes'?

a Jackson Browne
b Nils Lofgren
c Bob Dylan

Q2
Born with a wig and make-up?
Dolly Parton

QUESTION 3 *(3 POINTS)*

The Jackson Five changed their name on all record releases from 1977 to what?

a The Jackson Family
b The Jacksons
c Michael Jackson and The Jackson Four

Q3
The man who enjoyed playing to a captive audience?
Johnny Cash

QUESTION 4 *(7 POINTS)*

Which was the group's only No.1 single?

a 'Blame It On The Boogie'
b 'Shake Your Body (Down To The Ground)'
c 'Show You The Way To Go'

Q4
The man making art?
Phil Spector

QUESTION 5 *(4 POINTS)*

Jackie, Michael, Tito, Marlon and Jermaine: who's missing?

a Randy
b Frankie
c Johnny

Q5
The Irish joker?
Phil Lynott

answers

QUIZ 083

WHAT CAME NEXT?

From the info provided, complete the sequences to bag 25 more points.

Q1
'Sunshine Day'
was by
c Osibisa

Q2
'Summer Night
City' was a Top 5
hit for
a Abba

Q3
Suffering from
'Sunburn' was
b Graham
Gouldman

Q4
'Sunshine After
The Rain' was
from
b Elkie Brooks

Q5
The North
American
singer?
b Bobby Goldsboro

QUESTION 1 *(5 POINTS)*
Who hit albums: Live At Leeds, Who's Next, then what?
a Meaty Beaty Big And Bouncy
b Who Are You
c Quadrophenia

QUESTION 2 *(5 POINTS)*
John Lennon hit albums: Mind Games, Walls And Bridges, then
what?
a Double Fantasy
b Shaved Fish
c Rock 'n' Roll

QUESTION 3 *(5 POINTS)*
Jimi Hendrix hit albums: Band Of Gypsies, The Cry Of Love,
then what?
a Hendrix In The West
b Experience
c Rainbow Bridge

QUESTION 4 *(5 POINTS)*
Rod Stewart hit albums: Sing It Again Rod, Overture And
Beginners, then what?
a Smiler
b Blondes Have More Fun
c Tonight I'm Yours

QUESTION 5 *(5 POINTS)*
Status Quo hit albums: Hello, Quo, then what?
a Rockin' All Over The World
b If You Can't Stand The Heat
c On The Level

THE EAGLES HAVE LANDED

QUIZ 084

Five questions devoted to the Californian, based supergroup.

QUESTION 1 *(5 POINTS)*

Which 70s Eagles release currently holds the record for the biggest-selling album in the USA?

a Hotel California
b Their Greatest Hits 1971-1975
c One Of These Nights

Q1

The Jackson Five's first UK hit was
c 'I Want You Back'

QUESTION 2 *(5 POINTS)*

Which BBC programme used Eagles track 'Journey Of The Sorcerer' as its theme tune?

a Howard's Way
b Not The Nine O'Clock News
c The Hitchhiker's Guide To The Galaxy

Q2

The 'Doctor My Eyes' writer?
a Jackson Browne

QUESTION 3 *(5 POINTS)*

Not an original Eagle band member, guitarist Joe Walsh was formerly in which of these three groups?

a The James Gang
b Sopwith Camel
c The Funk Brothers

Q3

The name in question was
b The Jacksons

QUESTION 4 *(5 POINTS)*

Which of these three original Eagles band members is the drummer?

a Bernie Leadon
b Don Henley
c Randy Meisner

Q4

The No.1 single?
c 'Show You The Way To Go'

QUESTION 5 *(5 POINTS)*

1979 saw the much anticipated follow-up release to Hotel California. What was the album's title?

a Long May You Run
b The Long Run
c The End Of A Long Run

Q5

The missing Jackson?
a Randy

GREAT OPENINGS

This quiz is all about identifying correctly the opening words of five massively famous 70s songs.

Q1
Next came
a Meaty Beaty Big And Bouncy

QUESTION 1 (4 POINTS)
Which hit single begins with these five words?
"Stuck inside these four walls".

Q2
Next came
c Rock 'n' Roll

QUESTION 2 (4 POINTS)
Which well-known 70s hit begins:
"It's a god-awful small affair"?

Q3
Next came
b Experience

QUESTION 3 (4 POINTS)
Which hard-driving hit kicks-off with the line:
"Oh here we are and here we are and here we go"?

Q4
Next came
a Smiler

QUESTION 4 (7 POINTS)
Which new wave anthem begins with the words:
"Saw Vietnam as a partisan and wished I'd never been"?

Q5
Next came
c On The Level

QUESTION 5 (6 POINTS)
Which late-70s hit starts with the lines:
"When I was young, it seemed that life was so magical. A miracle, oh it was beautiful, magical"?

CAPITAL CITY OF POP

Liverpool is officially the capital city of pop, producing more chart-topping acts than anywhere else in the world. Here are five questions which connect to records and songs coming out of the city on the River Mersey.

QUIZ 086

QUESTION 1 *(4 POINTS)*
Which Liverpool group was made up of members called McGough, McCartney, McGear and Gorman?
a The Scaffold
b Wings
c The Swinging Blue Jeans

Q1
Biggest-seller?
b Their Greatest Hits 1971-1975

QUESTION 2 *(5 POINTS)*
Ken Dodd was one of Liverpool's most successful recording artists. What was the title of his biggest 70s hit?
a 'Tears'
b 'Broken Hearted'
c '(Think Of Me) Wherever You Are'

Q2
'Journey Of The Sorcerer' theme?
c The Hitchhiker's Guide To The Galaxy

QUESTION 3 *(4 POINTS)*
Which former Beatle had a Top 10 hit with 'Give Me Love (Give Me Peace On Earth)'?
a Ringo Starr
b John Lennon
c George Harrison

Q3
Joe Walsh was formerly in
a The James Gang

QUESTION 4 *(6 POINTS)*
'You Are My Love' was a smash hit for which of these groups in 1976?
a Liverpool Express
b The Merseybeats
c The Liver Birds

Q4
The Eagles' drummer?
b Don Henley

QUESTION 5 *(6 POINTS)*
Who was the only artist to have a hit single with The Beatles' 'Here, There & Everywhere'?
a Cilla Black
b Emmylou Harris
c Nana Mouskouri

Q5
The Hotel California follow-up?
b The Long Run

93

QUIZ 089 SEVENTIES POP GENIUS

TOP THREE CHALLENGE
Select the year in question based on the Top 3 hits listed.

Q1
"Stuck inside these four walls"?
'Band On The Run' by Paul McCartney and Wings

QUESTION 1 *(4 POINTS)*
In the week ending 11 June in which year were the Top 3: Rod Stewart's 'I Don't Want To Talk About It' / 'First Cut Is The Deepest', the Sex Pistols' 'God Save The Queen' and Kenny Rogers' 'Lucille'.

a 1976 **b** 1977 **c** 1978

Q2
"It's a god-awful small affair"?
'Life On Mars' by David Bowie

QUESTION 2 *(5 POINTS)*
'You To Me Are Everything' by The Real Thing, 'The Combine Harvester (Brand New Key)' by The Wurzels and 'Silly Love Songs' by Wings were the Top 3 on 26 June in which year?

a 1974 **b** 1975 **c** 1976

Q3
"Oh here we are" etc?
'Rockin' All Over The World' by Status Quo

QUESTION 3 *(6 POINTS)*
'Hey Girl Don't Bother Me' by The Tams, 'I'm Still Waiting' by Diana Ross and 'Did You Ever' by Nancy and Lee were the Top 3 in September of which year?

a 1971 **b** 1972 **c** 1973

Q4
"Saw Vietnam as a partisan" etc?
'Working For The Yankee Dollar' by The Skids

QUESTION 4 *(5 POINTS)*
In October of which year were these singles the Top 3? 'Band Of Gold' by Freda Payne, 'Patches' by Clarence Carter and 'Black Night' by Deep Purple.

a 1970 **b** 1971 **c** 1972

Q5
"When I was young" etc?
'The Logical Song' by Supertramp

QUESTION 5 *(5 POINTS)*
March was the month, but in which year did 'Billy Don't Be A Hero' by Paper Lace, 'The Air That I Breathe' by The Hollies and 'The Most Beautiful Girl' by Charlie Rich form the Top 3?

a 1973 **b** 1974 **c** 1975

THE THING IN QUESTION

Five songs and five things that were the subject of those songs for you to reveal.

QUESTION 1 *(5 POINTS)*

In the Mixtures hit 'The Pushbike Song', which road did they ride on?

a "Down South Avenue"

b "Up Riverside Road"

c "Along Tenth Avenue"

QUESTION 2 *(5 POINTS)*

In the Four Seasons hit 'Silver Star' the hero is riding what?

a A motorcycle

b A Palomino

c The desert wind

QUESTION 3 *(5 POINTS)*

In Joni Mitchell's 'Big Yellow Taxi', what colour was the hotel in the parking lot?

a Pink

b Green

c Yellow

QUESTION 4 *(5 POINTS)*

Cliff Richard had "nothing but bad luck" since the day he saw what at his door in 1976 hit 'Devil Woman'?

a "the devil"

b "the cat"

c "the witch"

QUESTION 5 *(5 POINTS)*

In the opening lines to the Stranglers hit 'No More Heroes', Leon Trotsky gets an "ice pick" that does what?

a "cuts through his heart"

b "made his ears burn"

c "froze his elbows"

Q1
McGough, McCartney, McGear and Gorman?
a The Scaffold

Q2
Ken Dodd's biggest 70s hit?
b 'Broken Hearted'

Q3
'Give Me Love (Give Me Peace On Earth)' was a hit for
c George Harrison

Q4
'You Are My Love' was a smash hit for
a Liverpool Express

Q5
'Here There & Everywhere' was a hit for
b Emmylou Harris

QUIZ 089

Q1
The year in question?
b 1977

Q2
This Top 3 were from
c 1976

Q3
The September in question?
a 1971

Q4
This Top 3 were all in the October of
a 1970

Q5
March was the month. The year?
b 1974

PUNK PERFECT

If you're punk perfect you'll have no trouble in gaining a maximum 25 points from this round.

QUESTION 1 *(5 POINTS)*
Where did The Damned get their group name from?
a From the sc-fi movie Village Of The Damned
b From drummer Rat Scabies' tattoo
c From a pub in south London called The Damned and The Dame

QUESTION 2 *(5 POINTS)*
Which punk group had a keyboard player called Johnnie Fingers?
a The Lurkers
b The Boomtown Rats
c The Stranglers

QUESTION 3 *(5 POINTS)*
Whose classic line-up is this? Malcolm Owen, Vince Segs, Paul Fox and David Duffy.
a Subway Sect
b The Ruts
c The Vibrators

QUESTION 4 *(5 POINTS)*
In which band did bassist and so-called "first female punk star" Gaye Advert play?
a The Adverts
b The Plasmatics
c The Slits

QUESTION 5 *(5 POINTS)*
Who had a 1977 hit with 'White Punks On Dope'?
a The Clash
b The Ramones
c The Tubes

CLASSIC LINES

Five classic lyric snippets for you to sing in your head. Maximum points only for the artist AND the song.

QUESTION 1 *(5 POINTS)*

Which US band had a hit containing this: "The radio is blastin'. Someone's knockin' on the door. I'm lookin' at my girlfriend. She's passed out on the floor."

QUESTION 2 *(5 POINTS)*

Who considerately sang "More, more, more. How do you like it, how do you like it"?

QUESTION 3 *(5 POINTS)*

Who insisted: "I could be a teacher in a classroom full of scholars. I could be the sergeant in a squadron full of wallahs"?

QUESTION 4 *(5 POINTS)*

Which group appears to have overdosed on the happy pills with: "There's a reason for the sun shiny sky. And there's a reason why I'm feeling so high"?

QUESTION 5 *(5 POINTS)*

Who is responsible for this slice of gritty action? "The Sweeney's doing ninety 'cos they've got the word to go. They get a gang of villains in a shed up at Heathrow."

Q1

The road The Mixtures rode on?

a "Down South Avenue"

Q2

The hero is riding...

b A Palomino

Q3

Joni Mitchell's hotel was

a Pink

Q4

What did Cliff see at his door?

b "the cat"

Q5

The "ice pick" did this to Trotsky

b "made his ears burn"

answers

QUIZ 091

CLASSIC LINE-UPS
Five classic line-ups: five bands to name.

Q1
The origin of The Damned?
a From the sc-fi movie Village Of The Damned

Q2
Johnnie Fingers was keyboard player in
b The Boomtown Rats

Q3
Owen, Segs, Fox and Duffy?
b The Ruts

Q4
Bassist Gaye Advert was a member of
a The Adverts

Q5
'White Punks On Dope' was the work of
c The Tubes

QUESTION 1 *(5 POINTS)*
Who are these four musicians better known as? Pete Ham, Tom Evans, Mike Gibbins, Joey Molland.

QUESTION 2 *(4 POINTS)*
Ann and Nancy Wilson enjoyed two British hit albums in the 70s as who?

QUESTION 3 *(6 POINTS)*
Which group had brothers Robert and Ronald Bell at their core?

QUESTION 4 *(6 POINTS)*
The duo of John Fiddler and Peter Hope-Evans are better known as who?

QUESTION 5 *(4 POINTS)*
Martin Lee, Lee Sheriden, Sandra Stevens and Nicky Stevens did big things for Britain as a group called what?

STEVIE WONDER-FUL

25 points on offer if you can negotiate this round about Stevie Wonder with no faults or refusals.

QUESTION 1 *(5 POINTS)*
Which of these 70s classic Motown singles saw Stevie Wonder share writing credits?
a 'Easy' by The Commodores
b 'Nathan Jones' by The Supremes
c 'Tears Of A Clown' by Smokey Robinson and The Miracles

QUESTION 2 *(5 POINTS)*
In which US state was Stevie Wonder born?
a California
b Michigan
c Texas

QUESTION 3 *(5 POINTS)*
In which year did Stevie Wonder see his tribute to Duke Ellington ('Sir Duke') hit the UK singles chart?
a 1975
b 1977
c 1979

QUESTION 4 *(5 POINTS)*
Which Lennon and McCartney song gave Stevie a hit in 1971?
a 'We Can Work It Out'
b 'Eleanor Rigby'
c 'Day Tripper'

QUESTION 5 *(5 POINTS)*
Which of these three releases provided Stevie with his highest-placed UK hit album during the 70s?
a Innervisions
b Fulfillingness' First Finale
c Songs In The Key Of Life

Q1
The classic line in question?
'Mama Told Me Not To Come' by Three Dog Night

Q2
"More, more, more" etc?
'More, More, More' by Andrea True Connection

Q3
"Scholars" and "wallahs" was
Ian Dury and The Blockheads ('What A Waste')

Q4
The uplifting lyric came from
The Bellamy Brothers with 'Let Your Love Flow'

Q5
The gritty action?
'Cool For Cats' by Squeeze

QUIZ 095 SEVENTIES POP GENIUS

QUIZ 093

TRACKS LEAD TO TITLES

Five albums you need to arrive at by following the tracks and the clues. To get full points you need both the album title and act name for each of these questions.

Q1
Ham, Evans, Gibbins and Molland =
Badfinger

QUESTION 1 *(4 POINTS)*
'Steamroller', 'Fire And Rain' and 'Sweet Baby James' are from which 1970 studio album?

Q2
Ann and Nancy make
Heart

QUESTION 2 *(4 POINTS)*
'Bohemian Rhapsody', 'God Save The Queen' and 'You're My Best Friend' are all tracks on which 1975 release?

Q3
The brothers Bell were at the core of
Kool and The Gang

QUESTION 3 *(5 POINTS)*
'Dig A Pony', 'For You Blue' and 'The Long And Winding Road' all appeared on which 1970 studio album?

Q4
Fiddler and Hope-Evans are better known as
Medicine Head

QUESTION 4 *(5 POINTS)*
'Down In The Tube Station At Midnight', 'David Watts' and 'English Rose' were all tracks on which album recorded in 1978?

Q5
The quartet in question?
Brotherhood Of Man

QUESTION 5 *(7 POINTS)*
'Sultans Of Swing', 'Lions' and 'Down To The Waterline' all appeared on which 1978 hit album?

FIND THE BAND

Find the act responsible for the three albums in each of these five questions.

QUIZ 094

QUESTION 1 *(4 POINTS)*

Who released 70s LPs called Octave, A Question Of Balance and Out Of This World?

Q1
The hit was
c 'Tears Of A Clown' by Smokey Robinson and The Miracles

QUESTION 2 *(7 POINTS)*

Who released these albums: Rubycon, Force Majeure and Phaedra?

Q2
Stevie was born in the state of
b Michigan

QUESTION 3 *(4 POINTS)*

Who was responsible for hit albums titled Killer, Love It To Death and Muscle Of Love?

Q3
Stevie's tribute to Duke Ellington was in
b 1977

QUESTION 4 *(5 POINTS)*

Blues For Allah, American Beauty and Terrapin Station were all 70s albums by which group?

Q4
The Lennon and McCartney song?
a 'We Can Work It Out'

QUESTION 5 *(5 POINTS)*

The Impossible Dream, Tomorrow Belongs To Me and Penthouse Tapes are three 70s releases by who?

Q5
Stevie's highest-charting 70s hit album?
c Songs In The Key Of Life

QUIZ 095

COUNTRY COMFORTS

A chance to test your knowledge of country music.

Q1

The album in question?

Sweet Baby James by James Taylor

QUESTION 1 *(5 POINTS)*

Who topped the UK chart in 1975 with 'Stand By Your Man'?

a Dolly Parton

b Bobbie Gentry

c Tammy Wynette

Q2

All three tracks are from

A Night At The Opera by Queen

QUESTION 2 *(5 POINTS)*

'Rhinestone Cowboy' was a smash hit for which of these three country gentlemen?

a Willie Nelson

b Glen Campbell

c Neil Diamond

Q3

The 1970 studio album?

Let It Be by The Beatles

QUESTION 3 *(5 POINTS)*

Which of these three is the correct title of a Charlie Rich US chart-topper?

a 'The Most Beautiful Girl'

b 'American Beauty'

c 'Beautiful Truck Stop Girl'

Q4

All these tracks?

All Mod Cons by The Jam

QUESTION 4 *(5 POINTS)*

Crystal Gayle hit big in 1977 with which of these country classics?

a 'Don't It Make Your Brown Eyes Blue'

b 'Don't You Make My Green Eyes Blue'

c 'Don't It Make My Brown Eyes Blue'

Q5

Which 1978 hit album?

Dire Straits by Dire Straits

QUESTION 5 *(5 POINTS)*

Johnny Cash was married to which Carter family member?

a June Carter

b Rosanne Carter

c Carlene Carter

102

WHEN WAS THAT?

Three facts from a year in the 70s and three clues for each possible five points...

QUESTION 1 *(5 POINTS)*

George Harrison launches his own Dark Horse record label, singer-songwriter Nick Drake dies and Faye Dunaway marries J Geils Band member Peter Wolf. All this happened in which year?

a 1972 **b** 1974 **c** 1976

Q1
All three albums were the work of The Moody Blues

QUESTION 2 *(5 POINTS)*

Elvis and Priscilla Presley divorced, Alvin Stardust releases his first single ('My Coo, Ca, Choo') and Gram Parsons dies. Select the correct 12 months from these.

a 1971 **b** 1973 **c** 1975

Q2
Rubycon, Force Majeure and Phaedra? Tangerine Dream

QUESTION 3 *(5 POINTS)*

The movie Tommy premies in London, 'Funky Gibbon' by comedy trio The Goodies invades the chart and Tim Buckley dies in Santa Monica. All occurred in which of these three years?

a 1973 **b** 1974 **c** 1975

Q3
The albums in question? Alice Cooper

QUESTION 4 *(5 POINTS)*

'One Step Beyond...' by Madness is released, tragedy at a Cincinnati Who concert when 11 rock fans are trampled to death and the BBC brings back Juke Box Jury, hosted by Noel Edmonds. Which year?

a 1977 **b** 1978 **c** 1979

Q4
Blues For Allah, American Beauty and Terrapin Station? The Grateful Dead

---

QUESTION 5 *(5 POINTS)*

The Ramones, supported by Talking Heads, play London's Roundhouse, Steve Hackett leaves Genesis and Kenny Rogers tops the singles chart with 'Lucille'. Pick the correct year.

a 1976 **b** 1977 **c** 1978

Q5
The group responsible? The Sensational Alex Harvey Band

DECADE DEBUTANTS

A round with the focus on those that made their chart debuts in the 70s.

QUIZ 097

Q1
Topping the UK chart in 1975?
c Tammy Wynette

QUESTION 1 *(6 POINTS)*
Roy Wood's new band Wizzard made their chart debut with which hit?
a 'Angel Fingers (A Teen Ballad)'
b 'See My Baby Jive'
c 'Ball Park Incident'

Q2
The country gentleman?
b Glen Campbell

QUESTION 2 *(4 POINTS)*
Who arrived on the scene with a debut hit called 'Gaye'?
a Clifford T Ward
b Gilbert O'Sullivan
c Nick Drake

Q3
The correct Charlie Rich chart-topper?
a 'The Most Beautiful Girl'

QUESTION 3 *(6 POINTS)*
'The Pink Parker EP' was a debut singles chart entry for which of these three?
a Ray Parker Jr
b Lady Penelope and Parker
c Graham Parker and The Rumour

Q4
Crystal Gayle hit big in 1977 with
c 'Don't It Make My Brown Eyes Blue'

QUESTION 4 *(4 POINTS)*
Who had a one-hit wonder with 'Ain't No Stoppin' Us Now'?
a Jefferson Starship
b McFadden and Whitehead
c Brian Prothoroe

Q5
Johnny Cash was married to
a June Carter

QUESTION 5 *(5 POINTS)*
Which pop group started their chart career with a string of hits, beginning with 'Lay Your Love On Me' and 'Some Girls'?
a Racey
b Darts
c Abba

OPENING LINES

Five brilliantly crafted opening lines to five well-known 70s singles,
with 25 points at stake.

QUESTION 1 *(3 POINTS)*

"When you're weary, feeling small. When tears are in your eyes, I will dry them all." Four easy points if you identify both song and act.

Q1
The record launch, the death and the marriage all happened in
b 1974

QUESTION 2 *(6 POINTS)*

Maximum points if you know the song and the group who began a mid-70s hit with these words: "I met a devil woman, she took my heart away. She said I had it comin' to me, but I wanted it that way."

Q2
All three events took place in
b 1973

QUESTION 3 *(3 POINTS)*

"I remember when rock was young. Me and Suzie had so much fun." The song and artist for maximum points.

Q3
Tommy, 'Funky Gibbon' and Tim Buckley's death all occurred in
c 1975

QUESTION 4 *(7 POINTS)*

Who released this and what was it called? "Every day I spend my time, drinkin' wine, feelin' fine."

Q4
The year in question?
c 1979

QUESTION 5 *(6 POINTS)*

Identify the act and song for "There's no point in asking. You'll get no reply."

Q5
The correct option?
b 1977

QUIZ 101 SEVENTIES POP GENIUS

VARIOUS ARTISTS

Check out this completely random set of images and identify all five for 25 points.

Q1
Wizzard made their chart debut with
c 'Ball Park Incident'

Q2
'Gaye' was the debut hit for
a Clifford T Ward

Q3
'The Pink Parker EP' was a debut single for
c Graham Parker and The Rumour

Q4
The one-hit wonder was
b McFadden and Whitehead

Q5
The pop group in question was
a Racey

QUESTION 1 *(5 POINTS)*
Who is this 'operator'?

QUESTION 2 *(5 POINTS)*
Identify these five fresh-faced boys?

QUESTION 3 *(5 POINTS)*
A popular solo artist who's even bigger in the band.

QUESTION 4 *(5 POINTS)*
A heavenly musician.

QUESTION 5 *(5 POINTS)*
A man you'd expect to find on the beach.

MY HOME TOWN

Five famous 70s musicians in need of being shown the way home.

QUESTION 1 *(5 POINTS)*

Where was Ian Dury born?

a Dartford, Kent

b East Ham, London

c Upminster, Essex

QUESTION 2 *(5 POINTS)*

Which town gave birth to Paul Weller?

a Watford, Hertfordshire

b Woking, Surrey

c Greenwich, London

QUESTION 3 *(5 POINTS)*

Talking Heads frontman David Byrne was born where?

a Dumbarton, Scotland

b Vancouver, Canada

c Waterford, Republic of Ireland

QUESTION 4 *(5 POINTS)*

Where did Michael Hutchence first enter the world?

a Wellington, New Zealand

b Stoke-on-Trent, Staffordshire

c Sydney, Australia

QUESTION 5 *(5 POINTS)*

Which town gave birth to Graham Nash?

a Blackpool, Lancashire

b Los Angeles, California

c Didsbury, Greater Manchester

Q1

Song and act?
'Bridge Over Troubled Water' by Simon and Garfunkel

Q2

Song and group?
'You Ain't Seen Nothing Yet' by Bachman-Turner Overdrive

Q3

Song and artist?
'Crocodile Rock' by Elton John

Q4

The release and its title?
'In A Broken Dream' by Python Lee Jackson

Q5

Song and group?
'Pretty Vacant' by the Sex Pistols

AMERICAN PIE

An entire round devoted to just one song, the epic story that is Don McLean's 'American Pie'.

QUIZ 101

Q1
The 'operator'?
Jerry Garcia

QUESTION 1 *(6 POINTS)*
According to the second verse of the song, what month of the year made Don McLean "shiver"?

Q2
The five fresh-faced boys?
The Babys

QUESTION 2 *(4 POINTS)*
The song describes "the day the music died", but which person's death is a key part of the song?

Q3
The popular solo artist who's even bigger in the band?
Stevie Nicks

QUESTION 3 *(5 POINTS)*
What were the "good old boys" drinking?

Q4
The heavenly musician?
Jimmy Page

QUESTION 4 *(6 POINTS)*
What was [John] Lennon reading at the same time the "quartet practiced in the dark"?

Q5
The man you'd expect to find on the beach?
Neil Young

QUESTION 5 *(4 POINTS)*
The song's jester borrowed a coat from which famous movie actor?

SEVENTIES POP GENIUS **QUIZ 104**

THEM HEAVY PEOPLE

 Five questions with a heavy metal and hard rock bias.

QUESTION 1 *(3 POINTS)*
Which of these three bands is very definitely not a heavy metal or hard rock outfit?
a Montrose
b Van Halen
c Average White Band

QUESTION 2 *(6 POINTS)*
Which country do hard rockers Scorpion hail from?
a Australia
b Germany
c Japan

QUESTION 3 *(5 POINTS)*
Who replaced Ozzy Osbourne in Black Sabbath in 1979?
a Ronnie James Dio
b Ted Nugent
c Bruce Dickinson

QUESTION 4 *(7 POINTS)*
Who went solo with the album Street Machine and the single 'This Planet's On Fire (Burn In Hell)' / 'Space Station No.5'?
a Robert Plant
b Sammy Hagar
c Rob Halford

QUESTION 5 *(4 POINTS)*
What's the colour of Jimmy Page's famous Gibson Double-Neck guitar?
a Black
b Gold
c Red

Q1
Ian Dury was born in
c Upminster, Essex

Q2
The town that gave birth to Paul Weller?
b Woking, Surrey

Q3
David Byrne was born in
a Dumbarton, Scotland

Q4
Michael Hutchence first entered the world in
c Sydney, Australia

Q5
Graham Nash was born in
a Blackpool, Lancashire

QUIZ 103

Q1
Which month made Don McLean "shiver"?
"February made me shiver"

Q2
The person in question?
Buddy Holly

Q3
The drink combination?
"Them good old boys were drinkin' whiskey and rye"

Q4
Lennon's reading matter?
"Lennon read a book on Marx"

Q5
The actor?
"When the jester sang for the king and queen..."
James Dean

JOHN, PAUL, GEORGE AND RINGO

Five more fabulous Fab Four questions.

QUESTION 1 *(3 POINTS)*
Which Beatle walks bare foot across the zebra crossing on the cover of the 1970 No.1 album Abbey Road?
a George Harrison
b Paul McCartney
c John Lennon

QUESTION 2 *(5 POINTS)*
Which Beatle took the role of the Pope in Ken Russell's movie Lisztomania?
a Ringo Starr
b John Lennon
c George Harrison

QUESTION 3 *(6 POINTS)*
Which Beatles album topped the chart in June 1977?
a Rock 'n' Roll Music
b Love Songs
c The Beatles At The Hollywood Bowl

QUESTION 4 *(4 POINTS)*
Unreleased as a single until the 70s, 'Yesterday' finally made the Top 10 in which year?
a 1976
b 1977
c 1978

QUESTION 5 *(7 POINTS)*
Which legendary punk band included their version of The Beatles' song 'Help!' on the B-side of their first single release?
a The Sex Pistols
b The Stranglers
c The Damned

ANARCHY IN THE UK...
ANSWERS IN THE BAG

The answers should be in the bag for any self-respecting Pistols fan.

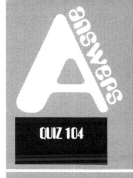

QUIZ 104

QUESTION 1 *(5 POINTS)*
Billy Idol, Steve Severin and Siouxsie Sioux were three of a south London group of Sex Pistols fans. What was the collective name for this group?

a The Crawley Collective **b** The Vauxhall Victims **c** The Bromley Contingent

QUESTION 2 *(4 POINTS)*
When Virgin released the Pistols and Great Train Robber Ronnie Biggs 'No One Is Innocent' as a double A-side single, what was on the flip?

a Sid Vicious's version of 'My Way' **b** The Sex Pistols' cover of 'Something Else' **c** Johnny Rotten's version of Pink Floyd's 'Money'

QUESTION 3 *(5 POINTS)*
Which member of the Pistols left to form The Rich Kids?

a Steve Jones **b** Glen Matlock **c** Paul Cook

QUESTION 4 *(5 POINTS)*
What was unusual about the band's last hit album of the 70s, Some Product – Carri On Sex Pistols, which peaked at No.6?

a It contained no music **b** It came in a silver foil sleeve **c** It was withdrawn from sale after one week

QUESTION 5 *(6 POINTS)*
What was Pistols manager Malcolm McLaren's birth name?

a Simon Arthur Andrew Gold **b** Malcolm Robert Andrew Edwards
c Graham Tyler Richard Andrews

Q1
Not a heavy metal or hard rock outfit?
c Average White Band

Q2
Scorpion hail from
b Germany

Q3
Replacing Ozzy Osbourne in Black Sabbath was
a Ronnie James Dio

Q4
The vocalist in question?
b Sammy Hagar

Q5
Jimmy Page's Gibson Double-Neck guitar is
c Red

SOUL SENSATIONS

Soul music was in plentiful supply in the 70s. Five groovy questions to bag 25 more points.

QUIZ 105

Q1

The barefoot Beatle?
b Paul McCartney

Q2

The Pope in Ken Russell's movie Lisztomania?
a Ringo Starr

Q3

The album in question?
c The Beatles At The Hollywood Bowl

Q4

'Yesterday' finally made the Top 10 in
a 1976

Q5

'Help!' appeared on the B-side of this band's first single
c The Damned

QUESTION 1 *(5 POINTS)*
Who released Black Moses, quit the Stax label for his own Hot Buttered Soul label and ended up reportedly bankrupt?
a Al Green
b Isaac Hayes
c Otis Redding

QUESTION 2 *(5 POINTS)*
'Soul Brother No.1' was the nickname of which legendary performer?
a Sam Cooke
b James Brown
c Percy Sledge

QUESTION 3 *(5 POINTS)*
Identify this performer from three soul clues. Born in Prattville, Alabama, recorded 'In The Midnight Hour' and died in 2006.
a Steve Cropper
b Wilson Pickett
c Aretha Franklin

QUESTION 4 *(5 POINTS)*
Who had a Top 20 hit in 1976 with 'Soul City Walk'?
a The Trammps
b Sly and The Family Stone
c Archie Bell and The Drells

QUESTION 5 *(5 POINTS)*
What was the logo on the legendary Stax record label?
a A cornet
b Clicking fingers
c Two satellites

EARLY ELTON

The biggest-selling pop act of the 70s, Elton John embraced West Coast rock, country and pop as the decade unfolded.

QUESTION 1 *(4 POINTS)*

Who was Elton's primary song-writing partner?

Q1
Billy, Steve and Siouxsie were all part of
c The Bromley Contingent

QUESTION 2 *(6 POINTS)*

True or false... John and Yoko's son Sean had Elton John as his godfather in 1975.

Q2
The flip side?
a Sid Vicious's version of 'My Way'

QUESTION 3 *(5 POINTS)*

In 1972, Elton and friends began their own record label. What was it called?

Q3
From Pistols to The Rich Kids?
b Glen Matlock

QUESTION 4 *(6 POINTS)*

Up until 1977, all Elton John's albums were produced by one man. Who was the man responsible for the work on LPs Elton John through to Rock Of The Westies?

Q4
The unusual last Pistols hit album of the 70s?
a It contained no music

QUESTION 5 *(4 POINTS)*

What was the name of the song dedicated by Elton to his record company's messenger boy, who died in a motorbike accident?

Q5
Malcolm McLaren's birth name?
b Malcolm Robert Andrew Edwards

QUIZ 107

WEDDING BELLS

Love and marriage is the subject, with 25 points to play for.

Q1
The soul star in question?
b Isaac Hayes

QUESTION 1 *(5 POINTS)*
Who is the bride? Formerly married to a Bee Gee, this Eurovision Song Contest winner married her hairdresser in 1977.
a Sandie Shaw
b Twiggy
c Lulu

Q2
'Soul Brother No.1' was the nickname of
b James Brown

QUESTION 2 *(6 POINTS)*
On which 70s Bob Dylan album is the track 'Wedding Song'?
a Street Legal
b Planet Waves
c The Basement Tapes

Q3
The three clues add up to
b Wilson Pickett

QUESTION 3 *(5 POINTS)*
In which year was the St Tropez wedding of Mick Jagger and Bianca Perez Morena de Macias?
a 1971
b 1973
c 1975

Q4
'Soul City Walk' was by
c Archie Bell and The Drells

QUESTION 4 *(4 POINTS)*
'Wedding Bell Blues' was a Top 20 hit for which 'Dimension'?
a The 1st Dimension
b The 4th Dimension
c The 5th Dimension

Q5
The Stax record label image?
b Clicking fingers

QUESTION 5 *(5 POINTS)*
What was the full title of the album of songs written by Eric Clapton while infatuated by his future wife Patti?
a Layla And Other Selected Love Poems by Derek and The Dominos
b Various Love Songs by Derek and The Dominos
c Layla And Other Assorted Love Songs by Derek and The Dominos

HIGHER OR LOWER?

Three singles in each question. Simply put them in the correct descending order according to their peak chart positions.

QUESTION 1 *(5 POINTS)*
One of these hits peaked at No.1, another at No.2, and one never got higher than No.3. Put them in the correct order
a 'The Show Must Go On' by Leo Sayer
b 'Indian Reservation' by Don Fardon
c 'Annie's Song' by John Denver

QUESTION 2 *(5 POINTS)*
One of these hits peaked at No.1, another at No.2, and one never got higher than No.3. Put them in the correct order
a 'When Will I See You Again' by The Three Degrees
b 'Sandy' by John Travolta
c 'Lady Eleanor' by Lindisfarne

QUESTION 3 *(5 POINTS)*
One of these hits peaked at No.1, another at No.2, and one never got higher than No.3. Put them in the correct order
a 'Let's Work Together' by Canned Heat
b 'Hang On In There Baby' by Johnny Bristol
c 'Figaro' by Brotherhood Of Man

QUESTION 4 *(5 POINTS)*
One of these hits peaked at No.1, another at No.2, and one never got higher than No.3. Put them in the correct order
a 'Monster Mash' by Bobby 'Boris' Pickett and The Crypt-Kickers
b 'Angel Fingers (A Teen Ballad)' by Wizzard
c 'Lola' by The Kinks

QUESTION 5 *(5 POINTS)*
You know the routine now - put these hits in the correct order
a 'Ride A White Swan' by T. Rex
b 'Woodstock' by Matthews' Southern Comfort
c 'Breaking Up Is Hard To Do' by The Partridge Family starring Shirley Jones and featuring David Cassidy

Q1
Elton's primary song-writing partner?
Bernie Taupin

Q2
Sean Lennon had Elton John as his godfather
True

Q3
The Elton and friends record label?
Rocket Records

Q4
Elton John's producer up until 1977?
Gus Dudgeon

Q5
Dedicated by Elton to his record company's messenger boy?
'Song For Guy'

STAND-OUT LINES

Correctly identify these stand-out lines from each of five chart-topping singles and 25 points are yours. Song AND artist in each case to claim the points.

QUIZ 109

Q1
The bride in question?
c Lulu

QUESTION 1 *(4 POINTS)*
"Wheels are made for rolling, mules are made to pack. I've never seen a sight that didn't look better looking back."

Q2
The Bob Dylan album track 'Wedding Song' is from
b Planet Waves

QUESTION 2 *(6 POINTS)*
"She ain't got no money. Her clothes are kinda funny. Her hair is kinda wild and free."

Q3
Mick and Bianca's wedding was in
a 1971

QUESTION 3 *(4 POINTS)*
"First I was afraid, I was petrified. Kept thinking I could never live without you by my side."

Q4
'Wedding Bell Blues' was by
c The 5th Dimension

QUESTION 4 *(5 POINTS)*
"Used to think that life was sweet. Used to think we were so complete. I can't believe you would throw it away."

Q5
The full title?
c Layla And Other Assorted Love Songs by Derek and The Dominos

QUESTION 5 *(6 POINTS)*
"It's cold outside, and the paint's peeling off of my walls. There's a man outside in a long coat, grey hat, smoking a cigarette."

SEVENTIES POP GENIUS QUIZ 112

RANDOM NOTES

A completely random set of questions that may or may not be right up your street.

QUESTION 1 *(5 POINTS)*

Sixties heart-throb Peter Noone (of Herman's Hermits fame) had a 70s solo hit with which of these songs written by David Bowie?

a 'The Laughing Gnome'
b 'Oh You Pretty Thing'
c 'Sorrow'

Q1
No.1 = c
No.2 = a,
No.3 = b

QUESTION 2 *(5 POINTS)*

'What Can I Say' and 'Lido Shuffle' are two mid-70s hits for which US solo star?

a Boz Scaggs
b Steve Miller
c Frank Zappa

Q2
No.1 = a
No.2 = b
No.3 = c

QUESTION 3 *(5 POINTS)*

What were Northern Soul group Wigan's Ovation doing in "the snow" in 1975?

a 'Surfing In The Snow'
b 'Skiing In The Snow'
c 'Standing In The Snow'

Q3
No.1 = c
No.2 = a
No.3 = b

QUESTION 4 *(5 POINTS)*

Supertramp's Breakfast In America album cover depicts a waitress holding aloft what?

a A guitar
b A map of America
c A glass of orange juice

Q4
No.1 = b
No.2 = c
No.3 = a

QUESTION 5 *(5 POINTS)*

Who is this Swiss-born keyboardist who recorded and performed with Yes and The Moody Blues and has had two UK solo hit albums.

a Jean-Michel Jarre
b Patrick Moraz
c Rick Wakeman

Q5
No.1 = b
No.2 = a
No.3 = c

OSMOND WORLD

Five questions on the family Osmond.

QUIZ 111

Q1

The stand-out
line in question
is from
'Wand'rin' Star' by
Lee Marvin

QUESTION 1 *(5 POINTS)*
**How many No.1 singles did Donny Osmond enjoy as a solo
performer?**
a 3
b 5
c 7

Q2

The line is from
'Love Grows Where
My Rosemary
Goes' by Edison
Lighthouse

QUESTION 2 *(6 POINTS)*
**Jimmy apart, all five remaining members of the Osmonds
extended singing family were born in which Utah town?**
a Ogden
b Tanner
c Sharples

Q3

The song in
question?
'I Will Survive' by
Gloria Gaynor

QUESTION 3 *(6 POINTS)*
Which Osmond is the most senior member?
a Jay
b Merrill
c Alan

Q4

The song and the
singer?
'We Don't Talk
Anymore' by Cliff
Richard

QUESTION 4 *(4 POINTS)*
**How old was Little Jimmy Osmond when his 'Long Haired Lover
From Liverpool' topped the singles chart in 1972?**
a Nine years and 251 days
b Thirteen years and 122 days
c Sixteen years and 87 days

Q5

This evocative
lyric line?
'Are 'Friends'
Electric' by Tubeway
Army

QUESTION 5 *(4 POINTS)*
What was Marie Osmond's only solo UK hit single?
a 'Deep Purple'
b 'Paper Roses'
c 'Make The World Go Away'

SEVENTIES POP GENIUS QUIZ 114

EUROVISION

Five Eurovision Song Contest questions from the competition's heyday.

QUIZ 112

QUESTION 1 *(5 POINTS)*
Who sang the winning entry for Ireland in 1970?
a Enya
b Johnny Logan
c Dana

QUESTION 2 *(5 POINTS)*
There have been some ridiculous winning song titles down the years. Which of these is a completely fabricated winning song?
a Israel's 'A Ba Ni Bi'
b Sweden's 'Kee Wee Dee-o, Ah!'
c The Netherlands' 'Ding-A-Dong'

QUESTION 3 *(5 POINTS)*
French singer Anne-Marie David performed for two different countries (winning once) in the 70s. Which were the two countries?
a Luxembourg and France
b Luxembourg and Israel
c France and Norway

QUESTION 4 *(5 POINTS)*
The United Kingdom finished third in 1973 with 'Power To All Our Friends'. Who performed the song?
a Cilla Black
b Cliff Richard
c Olivia Newton-John

QUESTION 5 *(5 POINTS)*
Katie Boyle is a name synonymous with the Eurovision Song Contest. In which year did she present her last show?
a 1974
b 1976
c 1978

Q1
The Peter Noone hit that Bowie wrote?
b 'Oh You Pretty Thing'

Q2
The US solo star?
a Boz Scaggs

Q3
Wigan's Ovation were
b 'Skiing In The Snow'

Q4
The Breakfast In America waitress was holding aloft
c A glass of orange juice

Q5
The keyboard player in question?
b Patrick Moraz

119

QUIZ 115 SEVENTIES POP GENIUS

THE ART OF ROCK

Weird imagery was rife on album covers in the 1970s. Picture these five works of art in your mind's eye and 25 points will be yours.

QUIZ 113

Q1
Donny's solo No.1s?
a 3

Q2
The Utah town in question?
a Ogden

Q3
Osmond senior?
c Alan

Q4
Little Jimmy Osmond was
a Nine years and 251 days

Q5
Marie Osmond's only solo UK hit single?
b 'Paper Roses'

QUESTION 1 *(7 POINTS)*
The description: a stage coach and horses stand under an unfinished motorway fly-over. What's the album and band?
a Holland by The Beach Boys
b The Captain And Me by The Doobie Brothers
c On The Border by the Eagles

QUESTION 2 *(4 POINTS)*
The description: a line illustration of a sheaf of corn. Album title and act for five points.
a Before The Flood by Bob Dylan
b John Barleycorn Must Die by Traffic
c Liege & Lief by Fairport Convention

QUESTION 3 *(5 POINTS)*
The description: two people bound and gagged in a fast-moving speedboat. The act name and the album title for five points.
a Propaganda by Sparks
b Horizon by the Carpenters
c Nilsson Schmilsson by Nilsson

QUESTION 4 *(4 POINTS)*
The description: a line of red shiny balls in a desert landscape. Which album does this cover appear on and who are the act?
a Manifesto by Roxy Music
b Court And Spark by Joni Mitchell
c Elegy by The Nice

QUESTION 5 *(5 POINTS)*
Description: a coastal painting featuring blue gulls, a shrouded figure and an elderly man in the foreground with a walking stick.
a Bursting At The Seams by The Strawbs
b Steve Winwood by Steve Winwood
c Hard Nose The Highway by Van Morrison

DAWNING OF THE DECADE

Five questions from the first year of the decade.

QUESTION 1 *(4 POINTS)*

Who had a Top 20 hit with 'Gasoline Alley Bred' in 1970?

a The Faces
b Alan Price
c The Hollies

Q1
The winning singer?
c Dana

QUESTION 2 *(5 POINTS)*

Mary Hopkin began the 70s with two Top 10 hits. The first was 'Temma Harbour', but what was the second?

a 'Those Were The Days'
b 'Knock Knock Who's There'
c 'Yesterday'

Q2
Completely fabricated?
b Sweden's 'Kee Wee Dee-o, Ah!'

QUESTION 3 *(6 POINTS)*

Which of these three singles was not a 1970 No.1 hit?

a 'Spirit In The Sky' by Norman Greenbaum
b 'Yellow River' by Christie
c 'You See The Trouble With Me' by Barry White

Q3
Anne-Marie David performed for
a Luxembourg and France

QUESTION 4 *(5 POINTS)*

In 1970, Easy Rider movie actor Dennis Hopper married which of these three rock stars?

a Michelle Phillips
b Mama Cass
c Janis Joplin

Q4
'Power To All Our Friends' was performed by
b Cliff Richard

QUESTION 5 *(5 POINTS)*

Do you know how many weeks in 1970 Bridge Over Troubled Water by Simon and Garfunkel was top of the album chart?

a 8 weeks at the top
b 13 weeks at the top
c 24 weeks at the top

Q5
Katie Boyle's final Eurovision Song Contest was in
a 1974

QUIZ 117 SEVENTIES POP GENIUS

QUIZ 115

POP MOVERS, SHAKERS AND SVENGALIS

A round involving the people behind the stars who made things happen.

Q1
The album cover in question?
b The Captain And Me by The Doobie Brothers

QUESTION 1 *(5 POINTS)*
Mickie Most was a highly successful record producer who masterminded his own record label throughout the 70s. Name it.
a Trojan
b RAK
c Swansong

Q2
The sheaf of corn cover?
b John Barleycorn Must Die by Traffic

QUESTION 2 *(5 POINTS)*
Which of these larger-than-life characters was the inspirational manager behind Led Zeppelin?
a Peter Grant
b Allen Klein
c Bill Graham

Q3
The speedboat cover artwork?
a Propaganda by Sparks

QUESTION 3 *(5 POINTS)*
Born on America's East Coast, David Geffen gravitated to the West Coast music scene and started his own label called what?
a Asylum
b Reprise
c Canyon

Q4
The red shiny balls in a desert landscape?
c Elegy by The Nice

QUESTION 4 *(5 POINTS)*
John Lennon and Yoko Ono credit themselves as two-thirds of the producer credits on Imagine. Who was the album's third producer?
a George Martin
b Phil Spector
c Tony Visconti

Q5
The coastal painting?
c Hard Nose The Highway by Van Morrison

QUESTION 5 *(5 POINTS)*
A&M was the largest independent label in the world during the 70s. The 'M' was co-founder Jerry Moss. Who was 'A', his partner?
a Herb Alpert
b Ahmet Ertegun
c Paul Anka

POLICE QUESTIONING

Five questions testing your knowledge of the trio that began when Sting and Stewart Copeland met Andy Summers in 1977.

QUIZ 118

QUESTION 1 *(5 POINTS)*

Which of the trio had formerly played with Zoot Money, Soft Machine and Eric Burdon's Animals before joining The Police?

a Sting

b Stewart Copeland

c Andy Summers

Q1
'Gasoline Alley Bred' was from
c The Hollies

QUESTION 2 *(4 POINTS)*

What was Sting's occupation in the two years leading up to the formation of The Police?

a Lawyer

b School teacher

c Coal miner

Q2
Mary Hopkin's second Top 10 hit of the 70s?
b 'Knock Knock Who's There'

QUESTION 3 *(5 POINTS)*

In 1979, Sting played which character in the mod movie Quadrophenia?

a Bisto

b Flash

c Ace

Q3
Not a 1970 No.1 hit?
c 'You See The Trouble With Me' by Barry White

QUESTION 4 *(5 POINTS)*

Where was the video for 'Walking On The Moon' filmed?

a The Kennedy Space Center in Texas

b The Science Museum in London

c The Giant's Causeway in Northern Ireland

Q4
Dennis Hopper married
a Michelle Phillips

QUESTION 5 *(6 POINTS)*

Who quit the band when they were briefly a four-piece, shortly after the arrival of guitarist Andy Summers?

a Henri Padovanni

b Hector Treesman

c Hal Gorkis

Q5
Bridge Over Troubled Water was
c 24 weeks at the top

GET STONED

With The Beatles disbanding ,the 70s proved to be fertile territory for The Rolling Stones as they set about proving that they were the best band in the world. How much do you remember?

QUIZ 117

Q1
The record label in question?
b RAK

Q2
The inspirational manager behind Led Zeppelin?
a Peter Grant

Q3
David Geffen's own label was
a Asylum

Q4
The third producer on Imagine?
b Phil Spector

Q5
The 'A' in A&M was
a Herb Alpert

QUESTION 1 *(4 POINTS)*
In which year did The Stones headline the Knebworth Festival?
a 1976
b 1977
c 1978

QUESTION 2 *(5 POINTS)*
What role did Prince Rupert Lowenstein perform for the band?
a Lawyer
b Producer
c Financial advisor

QUESTION 3 *(5 POINTS)*
Mick Jagger's moonlighting as actor in the film Performance produced a solo hit single called what?
a 'Letter To Michael'
b 'Memo From Turner'
c 'Message For Julie'

QUESTION 4 *(6 POINTS)*
Titled Monkey Grip, which member of the band was the first to release a hit solo album?
a Ron Wood
b Bill Wyman
c Keith Richards

QUESTION 5 *(5 POINTS)*
In which year did Stones singles 'Respectable' and the double A-side 'Miss You' / 'Faraway Eyes' hit the UK chart?
a 1976
b 1977
c 1978

SEVENTIES POP GENIUS **QUIZ 120**

I'M JUST A SINGER IN A ROCK 'N' ROLL BAND

Find the guy who does the most demanding job in each group listed below.

QUESTION 1 *(3 POINTS)*
Who fronted the Who?

QUESTION 2 *(7 POINTS)*
Who was the lead vocalist in Stiff Little Fingers?

QUESTION 3 *(5 POINTS)*
Name the frontsperson for prog rock band Yes.

QUESTION 4 *(6 POINTS)*
The lead singer in Magazine was who?

QUESTION 5 *(4 POINTS)*
Who fronted The Undertones?

Q1
Formerly with Zoot Money, Soft Machine and Eric Burdon?
c Andy Summers

Q2
Sting's occupation leading up to the formation of The Police?
b School teacher

Q3
Sting played
c Ace

Q4
The video was filmed at
a The Kennedy Space Center in Texas

Q5
The man who quit the band?
a Henri Padovanni

QUIZ 119

AFTER THE GOLD RUSH

Five tricky problems to solve on the subject of the 'Godfather of Grunge', one of rock's enduring characters.

Q1
The Stones headlined Knebworth in
a 1976

QUESTION 1 *(5 POINTS)*
Which of these is Neil Young's best-known nickname?
a Rocky
b Shakey
c Rusty

Q2
Prince Rupert Lowenstein was the band's
c Financial advisor

QUESTION 2 *(4 POINTS)*
Which of the following three was a former band in which Neil Young was a member?
a The Byrds
b Buffalo Springfield
c Poco

Q3
Mick Jagger's movie hit?
b 'Memo From Turner'

QUESTION 3 *(5 POINTS)*
'Heart Of Gold' was a stand-out track from which 70s Neil Young album?
a After The Gold Rush
b Harvest
c Tonight's The Night

Q4
Monkey Grip was a hit solo album for
b Bill Wyman

QUESTION 4 *(6 POINTS)*
What was the title of the protest song about the Kent State student massacre Young released with Crosby, Stills and Nash?
a 'Ohio'
b 'Chicago'
c 'Dallas'

Q5
'Respectable' and 'Miss You' / 'Faraway Eyes' hit the UK chart in
c 1978

QUESTION 5 *(5 POINTS)*
Young's favourite Gibson Les Paul guitar was nicknamed what?
a Old Faithful
b Old King
c Old Black

BRIAN TUNE PIE... AND OTHER ANAGRAMS

Another bunch of anagrams to unravel.

QUESTION 1 *(3 POINTS)*

Three easy points to kick-off with for this queen of rock.

MURDER FEY CRIED

QUESTION 2 *(6 POINTS)*

Make a first name and surname to create one half of a famous 70s musical partnership.

BRIAN TUNE PIE

QUESTION 3 *(5 POINTS)*

Two words spell the name of this US legend.

MONKEY OR BISONS

QUESTION 4 *(4 POINTS)*

A lover of the blues can be easily created from this.

CLIP ON TRACE

QUESTION 5 *(7 POINTS)*

Unravel this phrase for a two-word 70s frontman.

A KEY FLAG SHARER

QUIZ 123 SEVENTIES POP GENIUS

SAT OUR QUIZ?

Yes, it's more rock or pop legends jumbled up as anagrams.

QUIZ 121

Q1
Neil Young's
best-known
nickname?
b Shakey

Q2
The band in
question was
b Buffalo Springfield

Q3
'Heart Of Gold'
was from
b Harvest

Q4
The title of the
protest song?
a 'Ohio'

Q5
Young's favourite
Gibson Les
Paul guitar was
nicknamed
c Old Black

QUESTION 1 *(4 POINTS)*
Like the anagram suggests, he's more of a mum's favourite.

I VEXES DADS

QUESTION 2 *(6 POINTS)*
Decipher the name of the star in a US punk pop outfit.

BEARD BY HIRE

QUESTION 3 *(5 POINTS)*
He grew in stature and came to dominate the 70s music scene.

NOTED VIEWERS

QUESTION 4 *(5 POINTS)*
Re-assemble these three words to make a two-word bass player.

SAT OUR QUIZ

QUESTION 5 *(5 POINTS)*
Two words from these 13 letters will, with a bit of detective work, deliver-up this Paddington-born musician.

LOCO SITS LEVEL

WOODSTOCK THE MOVIE

Five questions about the 1970 movie of the 1969 festival.

QUESTION 1 *(4 POINTS)*
Which unusual cinematic feature did the movie use on general release?
a It was sepia tinted
b Split screen viewing
c Five different versions on release

QUESTION 2 *(5 POINTS)*
Which famous director was credited as an editor on the movie during his early film-making career?
a Martin Scorsese
b Oliver Stone
c George Lucas

QUESTION 3 *(6 POINTS)*
Name the iconic curly-haired Woodstock co-creator and promoter who famously rode the festival site on his BSA motorcycle.
a Country Joe
b Michael Lang
c Abbie Hoffman

QUESTION 4 *(5 POINTS)*
'Woodstock', the movie soundtrack song that appears in the film was performed and recorded by who?
a Matthews' Southern Comfort
b Joni Mitchell
c Crosby, Stills, Nash & Young

QUESTION 5 *(5 POINTS)*
Which Oscar category did the movie win?
a Best actor
b Best documentary
c Best director

QUIZ 122

Q1
Three points if you found
Freddie Mercury

Q2
One half of a famous 70s musical partnership?
Bernie Taupin

Q3
The US legend?
Smokey Robinson

Q4
The blues lover is
Eric Clapton

Q5
The frontman unravelled is
Feargal Sharkey

ROCK ARTEFACTS

Five signature pieces of rock memorabilia and 25 points at stake if you can identify them.

Q1
Like the anagram suggests, he's more of a mum's favourite
David Essex

Q2
The name of the star in a US punk pop outfit?
Debbie Harry

Q3
Who dominated the 70s music scene?
Stevie Wonder

Q4
The two-word bass player is
Suzi Quatro

Q5
The 13 letters arranged in the correct order gives
Elvis Costello

QUESTION 1 *(4 POINTS)*
Who famously had a custom-built 'superyob' guitar?
a Mick Jones of The Clash
b Dave Davies of The Kinks
c Dave Hill of Slade

QUESTION 2 *(5 POINTS)*
What colour was David Bowie's acoustic guitar on the legendary 'Starman' Top Of The Pops TV performance?
a Red
b White
c Blue

QUESTION 3 *(5 POINTS)*
Who famously wore an 'I Hate Pink Floyd' T-shirt?
a Roger Waters of Pink Floyd
b Johnny Rotten of the Sex Pistols
c Rick Wakeman of Yes

QUESTION 4 *(4 POINTS)*
What was generally accepted as being the most expensive piece of rock memorabilia when sold for almost $2.3 million (US)?
a John Lennon's white piano
b John Lennon's yellow psychedelic Rolls Royce
c John Lennon's black and white Rickenbacker guitar

QUESTION 5 *(7 POINTS)*
What was the venue of the earliest rock memorabilia auction raising money for US anti-war political campaigns in 1970?
a The Hollywood Bowl
b Madison Square Garden
c The Fillmore East

SEVENTIES POP GENIUS **QUIZ 124**

THROUGH THE KEYHOLE

In the style of the long-running TV show, try to reveal the rock star using a series of clues about the mansions, gaffs and cribs of the famous.

QUESTION 1 *(4 POINTS)*

A 'Woodside' mansion in Windsor, Berkshire: who's behind the keyhole?
a Eric Clapton
b Rod Stewart
c Elton John

QUESTION 2 *(6 POINTS)*

Which of these millionaire movers and shakers lived in a Totteridge Lane, North London mansion said to be the UK's largest residence?
a Mickie Most
b Brian Epstein
c Malcolm McLaren

QUESTION 3 *(7 POINTS)*

This homely artist titled his albums Mantle Pieces and Home Thoughts and had a hit single called 'Scullery'. Who is he?
a Robin Gibb
b Clifford T Ward
c Mike Batt

QUESTION 4 *(5 POINTS)*

In which county is 'Peel Acres', the cottage where broadcaster John Peel spent most of his life since the early 70s?
a Cambridgeshire
b Suffolk
c Lincolnshire

QUESTION 5 *(3 POINTS)*

Which country estate and house owned by the Cobbold family began hosting a series of rock concerts in the mid-70s?
a Knebworth
b Longleat
c Blenheim Palace

Q1
The unusual cinematic feature was
b Split screen viewing

Q2
The famous director credited as an editor?
a Martin Scorcese

Q3
The iconic curly-haired co-creator?
b Michael Lang

Q4
'Woodstock' the movie song was performed by?
c Crosby, Stills, Nash & Young

Q5
The Oscar category win?
b Best documentary

131

GREATEST HITS

25 points to be had based around the biggest hits of five 70s acts.

QUIZ 125

Q1
'Superyob' was
built for
c Dave Hill of Slade

Q2
David Bowie's
'Starman' guitar
was
c Blue

Q3
The T-shirt was
worn by
b Johnny Rotten of
the Sex Pistols

Q4
The piece of
memorabilia?
b John Lennon's
yellow psychedelic
Rolls Royce

Q5
The venue for
the earliest rock
memorabilia
auction was
c The Fillmore East

QUESTION 1 *(6 POINTS)*
Which of these three singles gave Nazareth their biggest hit in
the 70s?
a 'May The Sunshine'
b 'This Flight Tonight'
c 'Broken Down Angel'

QUESTION 2 *(4 POINTS)*
Three hit singles by The Dickies: only one of these made the
the Top 10. Which one?
a 'Paranoid'
b 'Nights In White Satin'
c 'Banana Splits (The Tra La La Song)'

QUESTION 3 *(5 POINTS)*
Pick the biggest hit from these three Isley Brothers 70s
chartbusters
a 'Harvest For The World'
b 'It's A Disco Night (Rock Don't Stop)'
c 'That Lady'

QUESTION 4 *(6 POINTS)*
Drummer Cozy Powell had three Top 20 hits in the 70s. Pick the
one that peaked the highest at No.3.
a 'Na Na' Na'
b 'Dance With The Devil'
c 'The Man In Black'

QUESTION 5 *(4 POINTS)*
Which of these O'Jays hits was their greatest with a highest
UK chart position of No.9?
a 'Back Stabbers'
b 'Brandy'
c 'Love Train'

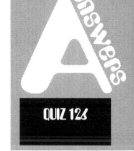

HOPELESSLY DEVOTED

Olivia Newton-John was the most successful solo female singer to grace the US Billboard Hot 100 in the 70s. Five questions to determine how much you know about the Cambridge-born singer and actress.

QUIZ 126

QUESTION 1 *(3 POINTS)*
In which country was Olivia raised from the age of five?
a Germany
b Australia
c USA

QUESTION 2 *(6 POINTS)*
Who wrote Olivia Newton-John's first UK hit, 'If Not For You'?
a Bob Dylan
b Paul Simon
c George Harrison

QUESTION 3 *(6 POINTS)*
Olivia Newton-John performed a song that finished fourth behind Abba's Eurovision-winner 'Waterloo' in 1974. Name her song.
a 'Long Live Love'
b 'Hopelessly Devoted To You'
c 'What Is Life'

QUESTION 4 *(5 POINTS)*
What was the 1977 one-word title single Olivia released that peaked at No.6?
a 'Ben'
b 'Joe'
c 'Sam'

QUESTION 5 *(5 POINTS)*
The 1978 smash hit duet 'You're The One That I Want' was released when Olivia was how old?
a 21
b 29
c 37

Q1
Behind the
keyhole?
c Elton John

Q2
The London
mansion was
home to
a Mickie Most

Q3
The home body
in question is
b Clifford T Ward

Q4
'Peel Acres' is in
the county of
b Suffolk

Q5
The country
estate and house
owned by the
Cobbold family?
a Knebworth

133

QUIZ 127

FIND THE LADY

A round exclusively involving 70s hits that all include a 'lady'.

Q1

The Nazareth
single was
c 'Broken Down
Angel'

Q2

The Dickies' Top
10 single was
c 'Banana Splits
(The Tra La La
Song)'

Q3

Biggest hit for
The Isley Brothers
in the 70s?
a 'Harvest For The
World'

Q4

Drummer Cozy
Powell's highest
charting hit?
b 'Dance With The
Devil'

Q5

The O'Jays'
biggest hit?
c 'Love Train'

QUESTION 1 *(4 POINTS)*
The Dire Straits 'lady' in question was which of these three creative females?
a 'Lady Writer'
b 'Lady Composer'
c 'Lady Painter'

QUESTION 2 *(4 POINTS)*
The Beach Boys had a Top 10 hit with which 'lady' in 1979?
a 'Lady Lisa'
b 'Lady Lynda'
c 'Lady Lucy'

QUESTION 3 *(6 POINTS)*
Who had a Top 5 hit with 'Lady Rose'?
a Diana Ross
b Jethro Tull
c Mungo Jerry

QUESTION 4 *(6 POINTS)*
Which of these three ladies was an early-70s hit for Herman's Hermits?
a 'Lady Barbara'
b 'Lady Love Bug'
c 'Lady Marmalade'

QUESTION 5 *(5 POINTS)*
Who sang about a 'Ladies Night' in 1979?
a LaBelle
b Kool and The Gang
c Clodagh Rodgers

134

SEVENTIES POP GENIUS QUIZ 130

NOT THEIR BEST WORK

This quiz explores the bargain bins for album releases by top 70s acts that were definitely not their best work.

QUESTION 1 *(4 POINTS)*
He Walks Beside Me, The Sun Years and Promised Land were albums that failed to excite all but the most devoted fans of?
a Johnny Cash
b Elvis Presley
c Chuck Berry

QUESTION 2 *(4 POINTS)*
Which hugely influential performer released these often forgotten albums? War Heroes, Crash Landing and Midnight Lightning.
a Mick Jagger
b Jimi Hendrix
c Neil Young

QUESTION 3 *(5 POINTS)*
Dandy In The Underworld, Zinc Alloy And The Hidden Riders Of Tomorrow and Futuristic Dragon are all lesser hit albums by who?
a Emerson, Lake And Palmer
b Marc Bolan / T. Rex
c Adam Ant / Adam and The Ants

QUESTION 4 *(6 POINTS)*
Making Love And Music, Pleasure And Pain and Sometimes You Win all charted but failed to match the single success for which group?
a Dr Hook
b Bee Gees
c Abba

QUESTION 5 *(6 POINTS)*
Drive On, Mad Shadows and Wild Life had their moments but all failed to make the Top 40 for which UK band?
a Paul McCartney and Wings
b The Shadows
c Mott The Hoople

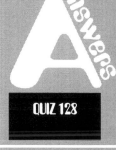

QUIZ 128

Q1
Olivia was raised in
b Australia

Q2
Olivia's first UK hit was penned by
a Bob Dylan

Q3
Olivia Newton-John's 1974 Eurovision Song was
a 'Long Live Love'

Q4
The one-word title?
c 'Sam'

Q5
Olivia was age
b 29

QUIZ 129

Q1
The Dire Straits
'lady' in question
was
a 'Lady Writer'

Q2
The Beach Boys'
'lady' was
b 'Lady Lynda'

Q3
The group with
the 'Lady Rose'
hit single were
c Mungo Jerry

Q4
The correct
Herman's
Hermits 'lady'
was
a 'Lady Barbara'

Q5
Who sang about
a 'Ladies Night'?
b Kool and The
Gang

QUIZ 131 SEVENTIES POP GENIUS

IN WHICH YEAR DID...?

Five different years with three clues for each and 25 points to be gained for a clean sweep.

QUESTION 1 *(5 POINTS)*
In which year did The Ruts hit with 'Babylon Burning', Madness make their chart debut and Minnie Riperton die?
a 1977
b 1978
c 1979

QUESTION 2 *(5 POINTS)*
Which year saw Jim Morrison die, Clodagh Rodgers reach No.4 with 'Jack In The Box' and the closure of the iconic Fillmore venues?
a 1970
b 1971
c 1972

QUESTION 3 *(5 POINTS)*
'Bang Bang' by B.A. Robertson almost tops the chart, Sid Vicious dies and Elton John asks 'Are You Ready For Love': pick the year.
a 1977
b 1978
c 1979

QUESTION 4 *(5 POINTS)*
In which year did Bruce Springsteen make his UK concert debut, Joe Walsh join the Eagles and Mud top the singles chart with Oh Boy'?
a 1975
b 1976
c 1977

QUESTION 5 *(5 POINTS)*
'Midnight At The Oasis' peaks at No.21, New York's Bottom Line club first opens and Patrick Moraz joins Yes in place of Rick Wakeman.
a 1973
b 1974
c 1975

SEVENTIES POP GENIUS QUIZ 132

WIDE EYED AND WHAT?

Five album or song titles all awaiting the correct choice.

QUESTION 1 *(4 POINTS)*
Andy Fairweather-Low was wide eyed and what in 1975?
a 'Wide Eyed And Wasted'
b 'Wide Eyed And Legless'
c 'Wide Eyed And Crushed'

Q1
The legendary
performer?
b Elvis Presley

QUESTION 2 *(7 POINTS)*
Chunga's what was the title of Frank Zappa's early-70s album?
a Chunga's Revenge
b Chunga's Arrival
c Chunga's Decline

Q2
The hugely
influential
performer?
b Jimi Hendrix

QUESTION 3 *(5 POINTS)*
Which Lucy was Marianne Faithfull singing about on her 1979 single?
a 'Lucy Auden'
b 'Lucy Troughton'
c 'Lucy Jordan'

Q3
The albums in
question were
all by
b Marc Bolan
/ T. Rex

QUESTION 4 *(4 POINTS)*
Overture And what was the title of the 1974 Faces album?
a Overture And Orchestra
b Overture And Climax
c Overture And Beginners

Q4
Not their best
work but all by
a Dr Hook

QUESTION 5 *(5 POINTS)*
Joan Armatrading's 1977 album was called what?
a Show Your Emotion
b Show Some Emotion
c Show My Emotion

Q5
None of the
albums listed
made the Top 40
but all were by
c Mott The Hoople

INTERNATIONAL BRIGHT YOUNG THINGS

A round connected to overseas pop making an impression over here.

QUIZ 131

Q1
All three events were in the year
c 1979

Q2
The year in question?
b 1971

Q3
Another rock death and two significant chart hits, all from
c 1979

Q4
A UK concert debut, a new Eagle and Mud go top, all in
a 1975

Q5
Three key events, all from
b 1974

QUESTION 1 *(4 POINTS)*
Which country do Ironhorse, Terry Jacks and Gordon Lightfoot share as their homeland?
a Canada
b New Zealand
c USA

QUESTION 2 *(5 POINTS)*
Golden Earring hailed from which European country?
a Belgium
b Holland
c Switzerland

QUESTION 3 *(5 POINTS)*
French-born Eurovision singer Anne-Marie David hit the UK chart in 1973 for nine weeks. Which of the following is her only UK hit?
a 'Wonderland'
b 'Wonderful Dream'
c 'Dreams'

QUESTION 4 *(5 POINTS)*
Which of these three French artists had a Top 10 UK hit with 'Black Is Black'?
a Bimbo Jet
b Space
c La Belle Epoque

QUESTION 5 *(6 POINTS)*
The Mixtures had a massive hit with 'The Pushbike Song' in 1971, but where did they come from?
a Jamaica
b Australia
c Germany

THE GROUP IN QUESTION

Five lists of 70s group members to get the grey matter working.

`QUIZ 132`

QUESTION 1 *(4 POINTS)*
Recognise the collective name for Terry Sylvester, Allan Clarke, Tony Hicks, Bobby Elliott and Bernie Calvert?

QUESTION 2 *(4 POINTS)*
Dennis Coulson, Tom McGuinness, Hughie Flint, Benny Gallagher and Graham Lyle was the line-up of which early-70s band?

QUESTION 3 *(6 POINTS)*
Name the band made up of Willy DeVille, Thomas R. Allen, Junior, Louis X. Erlanger and Ruben Siguenza.

QUESTION 4 *(7 POINTS)*
Who were the late-70s US outfit who lined up as Fee Waybill, Bill 'Sputnik' Spooner, Roger Steen, Prairie Prince, Michael Cotten, Vince Welnick and Rick Anderson?

QUESTION 5 *(4 POINTS)*
Rick Danko, Levon Helm, Richard Manuel, Garth Hudson and Robbie Robertson were who?

Q1
Andy Fairweather-Low was
b 'Wide Eyed And Legless'

Q2
Frank Zappa's early-70s album title?
a Chunga's Revenge

Q3
Marianne Faithfull was singing about
c 'Lucy Jordan'

Q4
The 1974 Faces album title?
c Overture And Beginners

Q5
Joan Armatrading's album title?
b Show Some Emotion

QUIZ 135 SEVENTIES POP GENIUS

STATES OF MIND

All about America, with 25 points on offer if you can answer these stateside questions correctly.

Q1
The country in question?
a Canada

Q2
Golden Earring hailed from
b Holland

Q3
Anne-Marie David's only UK hit?
b 'Wonderful Dream'

Q4
'Black Is Black' was by
c La Belle Epoque

Q5
The Mixtures were from
b Australia

QUESTION 1 *(5 POINTS)*
Whose 'American Girl' was released in 1977?
a The Allman Brothers Band
b Creedence Clearwater Revival
c Tom Petty and The Heartbreakers

QUESTION 2 *(4 POINTS)*
UK prog rockers Yes covered it, but who charted with 'America' the hit single in 1972?
a Genesis
b Simon And Garfunkel
c Emerson, Lake And Palmer

QUESTION 3 *(5 POINTS)*
Who had a Top 20 hit with 'American Woman' in 1970?
a The Guess Who
b Steppenwolf
c Steve Miller Band

QUESTION 4 *(7 POINTS)*
The group with the name America were a trio. Which of these three trios is the correct line-up?
a Martin Dooley, Greg Bakersfield and Philip Portland
b Matt Simon, Chet Reece and Rock Albertson
c Gerry Beckley, Dewey Bunnell and Dan Peek

QUESTION 5 *(4 POINTS)*
The song 'America', written by Leonard Bernstein, is from which musical?
a West Side Story
b Carousel
c On The Town

SEVENTIES POP GENIUS `QUIZ 134`

IN THE CHART AND ON THE NEWS

Select the correct month and year from the tunes and news clues.

QUIZ 134

QUESTION 1 *(5 POINTS)*
'Don't Give Up On Us' by David Soul tops the chart and Jimmy Carter pardons Vietnam draft dodgers. Choose the month and year.
a October 1975
b January 1977
c March 1979

QUESTION 2 *(5 POINTS)*
'Bright Eyes' by Art Garfunkel is No.1 and Margaret Thatcher becomes the first British female Prime Minister. Which date fits?
a December 1975
b June 1977
c May 1979

QUESTION 3 *(5 POINTS)*
'Everything I Own' by Ken Boothe is the chart-topper on the day Ali beats Foreman in boxing's 'Rumble In The Jungle'. When?
a September 1972
b October 1974
c July 1976

QUESTION 4 *(5 POINTS)*
'Bohemian Rhapsody' by Queen is No.1 while Steven Spielberg's Jaws smashes movie box-office records. Choose the right date.
a January 1976
b August 1977
c February 1978

QUESTION 5 *(5 POINTS)*
'My Sweet Lord' by George Harrison is the best-selling single as Britain adopts decimal currency for the first time, but when?
a April 1970
b February 1971
c November 1972

Q1
Sylvester, Clarke, Hicks, Elliott and Calvert were
The Hollies

Q2
Coulson, McGuinness, Flint, Gallagher and Lyle?
McGuinness Flint

Q3
DeVille and co were
Mink DeVille

Q4
The late-70s US outfit were
The Tubes

Q5
Danko, Helm, Manuel, Hudson and Robertson?
The Band

141

QUIZ 135

TROUBLED WATER

If you own a copy of Simon and Garfunkel's 1970 chart-dominating album Bridge Over Troubled Water, the next five questions should be a piece of cake.

Q1
'American Girl' was by
b Creedence Clearwater Revival

QUESTION 1 *(4 POINTS)*
Which of the following tracks did not appear on the album?
a 'Mrs Robinson'
b 'Keep The Customer Satisfied'
c 'Bridge Over Troubled Water'

Q2
'America' the hit single in 1972?
b Simon And Garfunkel

QUESTION 2 *(5 POINTS)*
On which record label was the album released?
a RCA
b EMI
c CBS

Q3
Charting Top 20 with 'American Woman' in 1970?
a The Guess Who

QUESTION 3 *(4 POINTS)*
Decades later, which UK solo artist released a hugely successful cover version of the album's third track, 'Cecilia'?
a Tom Jones
b Suggs
c Terry Hall

Q4
The trio America were
c Gerry Beckley, Dewey Bunnell and Dan Peek

QUESTION 4 *(5 POINTS)*
'The Only Living Boy In New York' is reportedly by Paul Simon about the time Art Garfunkel left him behind In NY to act in which movie?
a Midnight Cowboy
b Catch-22
c The Magic Christian

Q5
The musical in question was
a West Side Story

QUESTION 5 *(7 POINTS)*
The title track, when released as a single, carried an extra credit as part of the act name. Who joined Simon and Garfunkel?
a Simon and Garfunkel – Keyboard Billy Preston
b Simon and Garfunkel – Keyboard Larry Knechtel
c Simon and Garfunkel – Keyboard Hal Blaine

SEVENTIES POP GENIUS QUIZ 138

NUMBER ONE WRITERS

Songwriters mostly don't get the credit they deserve. Here's 25 points on offer if you can successfully name the wordsmiths responsible for five chart-topping hits.

QUIZ 136

QUESTION 1 *(6 POINTS)*
Who penned the first side of Rod Stewart's double A-side, 'I Don't Want To Talk About It'?
a Danny Whitten (Crazy Horse)
b Duane Allman (The Allman Brothers Band)
c Rusty Young (Poco)

Q1
The month and year in question?
b January 1977

QUESTION 2 *(4 POINTS)*
Who wrote the second half of Rod Stewart's double A-side, 'First Cut Is The Deepest'?
a Donovan
b Peter Tosh
c Cat Stevens

Q2
Both the clues point to
c May 1979

QUESTION 3 *(5 POINTS)*
Pick the correct songwriter for The Osmonds' 1974 No.1 'Love Me For A Reason'.
a Laurie London
b Johnny Bristol
c Scott Norfolk

Q3
'Everything I Own' and Ali beating Foreman both happened in
b October 1974

QUESTION 4 *(5 POINTS)*
Elvis Presley's 1970 chart-topper 'The Wonder Of You' was written by whom?
a Ronnie Hilton
b Dolly Parton
c Baker Knight

Q4
'Bohemian Rhapsody' and Jaws?
a January 1976

QUESTION 5 *(5 POINTS)*
Select the correct writer behind the Telly Savalas No.1 'If'?
a Mike Nesmith
b David Gates
c Charlie Chaplin

Q5
The No.1 hit and event in question were both from
b February 1971

QUIZ 139 SEVENTIES POP GENIUS

SAID BY WHO?

More quotes from some very opinionated and colourful characters.

Q1
The track not appearing was
a 'Mrs Robinson'

Q2
The label in question?
c CBS

Q3
The 'Cecilia' cover was by
b Suggs

Q4
The Garfunkel movie?
b Catch-22

Q5
The credit?
b Simon and Garfunkel – Keyboard Larry Knechtel

QUESTION 1 *(5 POINTS)*
Who summed herself up as: "A symbol of the scarlet woman, that was my claim to fame"?
a Dusty Springfield
b Marianne Faithfull
c Chrissie Hynde

QUESTION 2 *(5 POINTS)*
Which punk provided the quote "We have a lot to say and we say it fast."?
a Joey Ramone
b Rat Scabies
c Jimmy Pursey

QUESTION 3 *(5 POINTS)*
Who said "When I'm at the piano writing a song, I like to think I'm a man, not physically but in the areas that they explore."?
a Joni Mitchell
b Carole King
c Kate Bush

QUESTION 4 *(5 POINTS)*
"Music has been through a rather boring patch, but I think it's getting exciting again now." Who said this in Sounds in May 1977?
a John Peel
b Bob Harris
c Dave Lee-Travis

QUESTION 5 *(5 POINTS)*
Who confidently asserted: "If I wasn't me, I would have idolised myself in The Velvets."?
a Robert Fripp
b Lou Reed
c Andy Warhol

SEVENTIES POP GENIUS QUIZ 140

SEQUENCES

Five questions involving a correct sequence of events. Simply arrange the albums or singles in the correct chronological order.

QUESTION 1 *(5 POINTS)*
Here are three albums. Just place them in the correct order they hit the UK chart.
a Songs For Beginners (Graham Nash)
b Ooh La La (The Faces)
c Scared To Dance (The Skids)

Q1
The songwriter in question?
a Danny Whitten (Crazy Horse)

QUESTION 2 *(5 POINTS)*
Pick the correct order for these three No.1 singles.
a 'We Don't Talk Anymore' (Cliff Richard)
b 'Space Oddity' (re-issue) (David Bowie)
c 'School's Out' (Alice Cooper)

Q2
'First Cut Is The Deepest' was penned by
c Cat Stevens

QUESTION 3 *(5 POINTS)*
Three more albums. Select the correct chart entry order for these three.
a In The City (The Jam)
b Transformer (Lou Reed)
c Some Girls (The Rolling Stones)

Q3
The Osmonds' No.1 writer in question?
b Johnny Bristol

QUESTION 4 *(5 POINTS)*
Three classic hit singles. Pick the right order for five more points.
a 'If You Don't Know Me By Now' (Harold Melvin and The Bluenotes)
b 'Tiger Feet' (Mud)
c 'Leaving On A Jet Plane' (Peter, Paul and Mary)

Q4
Elvis Presley's 1970 chart-topper was the work of
c Baker Knight

QUESTION 5 *(5 POINTS)*
Three big albums to place in date order.
a Harvest (Neil Young)
b Abraxas (Santana)
c Going For The One (Yes)

Q5
'If' was written by
b David Gates

145

JACKO GOES SOLO

Five questions picked from facts involving Michael Jackson's 70s solo career.

QUIZ 139

Q1
The woman in question?
b Marianne Faithfull

Q2
"We have a lot to say and we say it fast" were the words of
b Rat Scabies

Q3
This revealing quote was from
c Kate Bush

Q4
Expressing his feelings about a brighter future for music was
a John Peel

Q5
These less than modest words came from
b Lou Reed

QUESTION 1 *(5 POINTS)*
In which year did 'Got To Be There' signal the start of Michael Jackson's UK solo career?
a 1970
b 1972
c 1974

QUESTION 2 *(4 POINTS)*
Michael Jackson had a million-selling US No.1 with 'Ben', from the movie of the same name. What was the film about?
a A superhero Alsatian dog
b A cartoon spaceman
c A boy and his pet rat

QUESTION 3 *(6 POINTS)*
Off The Wall led to super stardom for Jackson when it charted in September 1979. How old was he on his birthday a month earlier?
a 19
b 21
c 23

QUESTION 4 *(5 POINTS)*
Which character did Michael Jackson play in the 70s movie The Wiz?
a Tin Man
b Lion
c Scarecrow

QUESTION 5 *(5 POINTS)*
How many solo No.1 singles did Jackson enjoy in the UK chart during the 70s?
a None
b 2
c 4

SEVENTIES POP GENIUS QUIZ 142

WHAT'S MISSING?

Five missing words from well-known 70s singles and album titles.

QUESTION 1 *(5 POINTS)*

'Baby _____' was the No.1 follow-up to 'In The Summertime' for Mungo Jerry. What's the missing word?

a Jump

b Please

c Dive

QUESTION 2 *(5 POINTS)*

What's missing from this 1977 Tubes single title?
'White _____ On Dope'.

a Boys

b Dogs

c Punks

QUESTION 3 *(4 POINTS)*

How did the 1972 Gilbert O'Sullivan hit 'Ooh-Wakka-Doo-Wakka-_____' end?

a 'Ooh-Wakka-Doo-Wakka-Day'

b 'Ooh-Wakka-Doo-Wakka-Doo'

c 'Ooh-Wakka-Doo-Wakka-Dum'

QUESTION 4 *(6 POINTS)*

Which hotel did The Grateful Dead check into on the album Grateful Dead From The _____ Hotel?

a Grateful Dead From The Earth Hotel

b Grateful Dead From The Mercury Hotel

c Grateful Dead From The Mars Hotel

QUESTION 5 *(5 POINTS)*

Select the version with the correct missing word from Emerson, Lake and Palmer's LP Brain _____ Surgery.

a Brain Sugar Surgery

b Brain Salad Surgery

c Brain Strain Surgery

QUIZ 140

Q1
The correct order?
a b c

Q2
First, second and third?
c b a

Q3
The correct chart entry order was
b a c

Q4
The classic hit order?
c a b

Q5
First to last, the albums were in this order
b a c

147

QUIZ 143 SEVENTIES POP GENIUS

COLLABORATIONS
You can nab 25 points with a decent knowledge of pop and rock duets.

The start of Michael Jackson's UK solo career?
b 1972

The movie's subject matter?
c A boy and his pet rat

Michael Jackson's age a month before the release of Off The Wall?
b 21

Michael Jackson's character in The Wiz?
c The Scarecrow

Michael Jackson's UK chart-topping solo singles in the 70s?
a None

QUESTION 1 *(5 POINTS)*
Which two members of supergroup Crosby, Stills, Nash and Young collaborated as a duo on 70s album Long May You Run.
a Stephen Stills and Neil Young
b Graham Nash and David Crosby
c Graham Nash and Neil Young

QUESTION 2 *(4 POINTS)*
'Then Came You' was a collaboration between Dionne Warwicke and who?
a Dionne Warwicke and Elton John
b Dionne Warwicke and The Detroit Spinners
c Dionne Warwicke and The Temptations

QUESTION 3 *(4 POINTS)*
Who joined Diana Ross on the 1974 smash hit 'You Are Everything'?
a Diana Ross and Stevie Wonder
b Diana Ross and Michael Jackson
c Diana Ross and Marvin Gaye

QUESTION 4 *(7 POINTS)*
What was the correct collaboration credit on the Linda Carr hit 'Highwire'?
a Linda Carr and The Girls' Station
b Linda Carr and The Shadows
c Linda Carr and The Love Squad

QUESTION 5 *(5 POINTS)*
Who joined Stephanie De Sykes on No.2 hit 'Born With A Smile On My Face'?
a Stephanie De Sykes and Lynsey De Paul
b Stephanie De Sykes and Rain
c Stephanie De Sykes and Curved Air

SEVENTIES POP GENIUS QUIZ 144

FIVE QUESTION MARKS

All five questions involve song titles that are themselves questions.

QUIZ 142

QUESTION 1 *(4 POINTS)*
Name the only 70s Slade hit single title that was a question.

Q1
**The missing
word is**
a Jump

QUESTION 2 *(5 POINTS)*
**Who asked "Why, Oh Why, Oh Why?" in the title of a 1973 Top
10 hit?**

Q2
**The missing
word is**
c Punks

QUESTION 3 *(5 POINTS)*
**'Which Way Is Up' asked which act in the 'Theme Song From
'Which Way Is Up" in 1978, and then asked 'What You Waitin' For'
later the same year?**

Q3
**The full title with
the last word
added reads**
a 'Ooh-Wakka-
Doo-Wakka-Day'

QUESTION 4 *(5 POINTS)*
**What question formed the title of Dawn and Tony Orlando's
follow-up hit to 'Knock Three Times'?**

Q4
**The hotel in
question?**
c Grateful Dead
From The Mars
Hotel

QUESTION 5 *(6 POINTS)*
'Who Killed Bambi' in 1979?

Q5
**The correct
version?**
b Brain Salad
Surgery

DAMNED LIES (OR ARE THEY?)

More questions of reality versus fiction.

Q1
The two members in question?
a Stephen Stills and Neil Young

Q2
Warwicke teamed up with
b The Detroit Spinners

Q3
Diana's duet partner was
c Marvin Gaye

Q4
The correct collaboration?
c Linda Carr and The Love Squad

Q5
The No.2 hit duo featured
b Rain

QUESTION 1 *(5 POINTS)*
Those 'Living Next Door To Alice' lads Smokie were actually spelled Smokey for their first two Top 10 hits.
a True
b False

QUESTION 2 *(5 POINTS)*
Pop star Hurricane Smith was in reality Norman Smith, a recording engineer and producer who had worked with The Beatles.
a True
b False

QUESTION 3 *(5 POINTS)*
Clash legend Joe Strummer was born in Tasmania.
a True
b False

QUESTION 4 *(5 POINTS)*
'Jimmy Jimmy' was The Undertones' highest-placed 70s chart hit.
a True
b False

QUESTION 5 *(5 POINTS)*
Rod Stewart is a self-confessed fanatical model railway modeller in his spare time.
a True
b False

HOW LONG?

'How Long' sang Ace in 1974, inspiring this quiz all about the march of time.

QUIZ 144

QUESTION 1 *(5 POINTS)*
The longest track on the Led Zeppelin IV album, what was the actual length of classic track 'Stairway To Heaven'?
a 16 minutes, 52 seconds
b 12 minutes, 19 seconds
c 8 minutes, 2 seconds

QUESTION 2 *(5 POINTS)*
How many consecutive weeks did Paul McCartney and Wings' Band On The Run stay top of the album chart for 1974?
a Three weeks
b Seven weeks
c Eleven weeks

QUESTION 3 *(4 POINTS)*
'The Time Warp' was a tune from which 1970s musical?
a The Rocky Horror Show
b Tommy
c Jesus Christ Superstar

QUESTION 4 *(5 POINTS)*
The 70s life-span of the Sex Pistols was restricted to two short years. In which year did they split?
a 1977
b 1978
c 1979

QUESTION 5 *(6 POINTS)*
In 1974, Supertramp's debut hit album was the crime of what period of time?
a Crime Of The Century
b Crime Of The Year
c Crime Of The Decade

Q1
Slade's question?
'How Does It Feel'

Q2
Asking why was.
Gilbert O'Sullivan

Q3
Asking all the questions were
Stargard

Q4
The follow-up single was
'What Are You Doing Sunday?'

Q5
Killing Bambi were
Ten Pole Tudor: its flip side, was Sex Pistols' track 'Silly Thing'

FIRST FEW WORDS

More opening lines to classic hit singles. Points only for correctly arriving at both the right act and right track in each question.

QUIZ 145

Q1
"Smokey"
spelling?
a True

Q2
The Norman
Smith/Beatles
story is
a True

Q3
Joe Strummer:
born in
Tasmania?
b False. He was
born in Turkey

Q4
'Jimmy Jimmy':
their highest-
placed 70s chart
hit?
a True

Q5
Rod Stewart:
fanatical railway
modeller?
a True

QUESTION 1 *(5 POINTS)*
Which 1972 single opens with these famous lines? "Women think I'm tasty. But they're always tryin' to waste me. And make me burn the candle right down."

QUESTION 2 *(5 POINTS)*
"She keeps Moet et Chandon, in a pretty cabinet..." Who began their second hit single with these words?

QUESTION 3 *(5 POINTS)*
The song begins: "There she stood in the street, smiling from her head to her feet". Name the track and the act.

QUESTION 4 *(5 POINTS)*
A much-covered song that hit the UK chart by one of Britain's early 70s solo superstars in July 1970. "Give me a ticket for an aeroplane. I ain't got time to take a fast train."

QUESTION 5 *(5 POINTS)*
Whose dance move instructions are these? "Choose yourself a partner from the middle of the floor. Blow a little kiss to the woman next door..."

A WORD, PLEASE

In a complete role reversal from the last quiz, we give you the song and the artist and you come up with the words. In fact, all you need is the very first word in each case.

QUESTION 1 *(4 POINTS)*
First word only required for 'Walking On The Moon' by The Police.

Q1
'Stairway To Heaven' runs for
c 8 minutes, 2 seconds

QUESTION 2 *(5 POINTS)*
What's the opening word for The Commodores' 1977 classic 'Easy'?

Q2
The Band On The Run run was
b Seven weeks

QUESTION 3 *(6 POINTS)*
The Jam's last hit single of the 70s, 'The Eton Rifles', begins with which word?

Q3
'The Time Warp' was a tune from
a The Rocky Horror Show

QUESTION 4 *(5 POINTS)*
'Forever In Blue Jeans' was Neil Diamond's final hit of the 70s, but which word began this No.16 single?

Q4
The Sex Pistols split in
b 1978

QUESTION 5 *(5 POINTS)*
First word required from the festive favourite – 'Happy Xmas (War Is Over)' by John and Yoko and The Plastic Ono Band.

Q5
Supertramp's period of time?
a Crime Of The Century

REMEMBER 1979?

Mork and Mindy … Three Mile Island … Maggie enters No.10... Now test your pop knowledge on the final year of the decade.

QUESTION 1 *(5 POINTS)*
The Specials' eponymously titled debut album was released in October 1979. But, who was its well-known producer?
a Elvis Costello
b Dave Edmunds
c Pete Townshend

QUESTION 2 *(4 POINTS)*
1979 saw the Los Angeles premiere of the movie The Rose which was based loosely on the life of Janis Joplin. Who was its star?
a Buffy Sainte-Marie
b Bette Midler
c Judee Sill

QUESTION 3 *(6 POINTS)*
Boney M enjoyed one week at No.1 in September 1979. Which is the correct album title?
a Oceans Of Fantasy
b Fantasy Ocean Ride
c Riding The Fantasy Ocean

QUESTION 4 *(6 POINTS)*
Led Zeppelin's consecutive run of eight chart-topping albums came to an end in 1979. What was No.1 album number eight?
a Coda
b Presence
c In Through The Out Door

QUESTION 5 *(4 POINTS)*
In May 1979, Elton John made history by becoming the first solo rock or pop artist to tour where?
a China
b USSR
c Argentina

THE JUDGE DREAD QUIZ

One of the most banned musicians of the 70s, Judge Dread nevertheless managed 11 hit singles throughout the decade.

QUIZ 148

QUESTION 1 *(5 POINTS)*
Not surprisingly, the man known as Judge Dread wasn't born with that name. What name was on his birth certificate?
a Mark Hughes
b Alex Hughes
c Hugh Marks

QUESTION 2 *(5 POINTS)*
What was Judge Dread's only 70s hit album?
a Cactus Stories
b Judge Dread's Night Mare
c Bedtime Stories

QUESTION 3 *(5 POINTS)*
Judge Dread's first three hit singles were all prefixed by what word?
a 'Big'
b 'Huge'
c 'Small'

QUESTION 4 *(5 POINTS)*
Two are false, but which of these three statements is true?
a Judge Dread was more than 45-years-old when he had his debut 70s hit.
b Judge Dread was reported to be the first white man to have a reggae hit in Jamaica.
c Judge Dread once played professional football for Dutch club Ajax.

QUESTION 5 *(5 POINTS)*
Dread's 1975 Top 10 hit was his own very individual cover of which of these classics?
a 'Honky Tonk Women'
b 'Je T'aime (Moi Non Plus)'
c 'All You Need Is Love'

Q1
First word of 'Walking On The Moon'?
"GIANT steps are what you take…"

Q2
The opening word for 'Easy'?
"KNOW it sounds funny but I just can't stand the pain…"

Q3
The Jam hit start?
"SUP up your beer and collect your fags, there's a row going on down near Slough…"

Q4
'Forever In Blue Jeans' begins
"MONEY talks. But it don't sing and dance…"

Q5
John and Yoko's Christmas hit?
"SO this is Christmas. And what have you done…"

THE JOHNNY ROTTEN QUIZ

Five rotten Johnny brainteasers about one of the 70s most iconic figures.

QUIZ 149

Q1
The well known producer?
a Elvis Costello

Q2
The star in question?
b Bette Midler

Q3
The correct album title?
a Oceans Of Fantasy

Q4
The Led Zeppelin album?
c In Through The Out Door

Q5
Elton's historic solo tour was to
b USSR

QUESTION 1 *(5 POINTS)*
Everyone knows he was born John Lydon, but where and when?
a Dublin in 1954
b London in 1956
c Glasgow in 1958

QUESTION 2 *(5 POINTS)*
Which artist name-checked the Sex Pistols frontman - "This is the story of Johnny Rotten" - in their 'My, My, Hey, Hey' album track?
a Neil Young
b Elton John
c Patti Smith

QUESTION 3 *(5 POINTS)*
When Lydon formed Public Image Ltd, the first line-up included who on bass guitar?
a Jah Wobble
b Keith Levene
c Glen Matlock

QUESTION 4 *(5 POINTS)*
Married to Nora Forster, Lydon was stepfather to another punk legend, Ari Up. Which group did she belong to?
a The 101ers
b The Slits
c The Deviants

QUESTION 5 *(5 POINTS)*
Bizarrely, Lydon, kitted-out as an English toff, advertised which of these brands in a TV and poster campaign in 2008?
a Marmite
b The National Trust
c Country Life butter

THE TITLE IS ALL THEY HAVE IN COMMON

Songs that share the same name, but little else.

QUESTION 1 *(5 POINTS)*
'Substitute' turned out to be The Who's highest-placed hit in the 70s at No.7. Who had a bigger hit with a different 'Substitute'?
a Space
b Boris Gardiner
c Clout

QUESTION 2 *(5 POINTS)*
Dan Hartman had a hit with 'This Is It', but who had an even higher placed one with a different song of the same name?
a Melba Moore
b R. Dean Taylor
c Elton John

QUESTION 3 *(5 POINTS)*
Two different 'Angels': Aretha Franklin's 'Angel' stalled at No.37, but whose 'Angel' registered a No.4 hit in 1972?
a Peter Gabriel
b Peter Frampton
c Rod Stewart

QUESTION 4 *(5 POINTS)*
'Love Me' was a modest Top 40 hit for Diana Ross, but who went Top 10 with a different 'Love Me' in 1976?
a Yvonne Elliman
b Bonnie Tyler
c Elkie Brooks

QUESTION 5 *(5 POINTS)*
1972 saw Neil Sedaka bag a No.19 place for his classic 'Oh! Carol'. Who took a different song of the same name to No.5 six years later?
a Status Quo
b Smokie
c Dr Feelgood

Q1
Judge Dread was born
b Alex Hughes

Q2
Judge Dread's only 70s hit album?
c Bedtime Stories

Q3
Judge Dread's first three hit singles were all prefixed by
a 'Big'

Q4
The truth?
b He was reported to be the first white man to have a reggae hit in Jamaica

Q5
Dread's 1975 Top 10 cover was
b 'Je T'aime (Moi Non Plus)'

PLACE NAMES IN POP

Five easy questions where you need to match the name to the place.

QUIZ 151

Q1
John Lydon was born in
b London in 1956

QUESTION 1 *(3 POINTS)*
The place in question comes courtesy of 'Philadelphia Freedom'. Who hit big with it in 1975?
a Sam Cooke
b Rod Stewart
c Elton John

Q2
The name-checking artist?
a Neil Young

QUESTION 2 *(5 POINTS)*
Who charted with 'Portsmouth' in 1976?
a John Noakes and Shep
b Mike Oldfield
c Sally Oldfield

Q3
The bass guitarist in question?
a Jah Wobble

QUESTION 3 *(5 POINTS)*
'Hollywood Nights' was a modest 70s hit for which group?
a Bob Seger and The Silver Bullett Band
b J Geils Band
c Motorhead

Q4
Ari Up's group was
b The Slits

QUESTION 4 *(5 POINTS)*
Who hit big with 'Parisienne Walkways' in 1979?
a Billy Joel
b John Miles
c Gary Moore

Q5
The ad campaign was for
c Country Life butter

QUESTION 5 *(7 POINTS)*
'Tuxedo Junction': who peaked at No.24 with the song in 1976?
a Gene Pitney
b Manhattan Transfer
c Captain and Tennille

VANISHING ACTS

The topic this time is acts that had just one solitary chart hit in the 70s but may or may not have made an impression in other decades.

QUIZ 152

QUESTION 1 *(4 POINTS)*
Just one 70s sighting in the singles chart for the man with 'Eighteen With A Bullet'.
a Pete Wingfield
b Peter Sinfield
c Chris Spedding

QUESTION 2 *(6 POINTS)*
Which Ruffin was responsible for the Top 10 hit 'Walk Away From Love'?
a Bruce Ruffin
b David Ruffin
c Jimmy Ruffin

QUESTION 3 *(4 POINTS)*
'Don't Leave Me This Way' was a No.13 hit for which of these three in 1977?
a The Hollies
b Thelma Houston
c The Pointer Sisters

QUESTION 4 *(5 POINTS)*
Whose one very prominent appearance in the 70s was with 'Snoopy Vs. The Red Baron'?
a The Goodies
b The Hotshots
c The Pipkins

QUESTION 5 *(6 POINTS)*
'Clog Dance' was a one-off Top 20 hit on the Jet label for whom?
a Paul Nicholas
b Pickettywitch
c Violinski

Q1
The bigger hitting 'Substitute' was by
c Clout

Q2
The more successful 'This Is It' was by
a Melba Moore

Q3
The 'Angel' in question was by
c Rod Stewart

Q4
The 1976 Top 10 'Love Me' was by
a Yvonne Elliman

Q5
The second 'Oh Carol' of the 70s was by
b Smokie

159

QUIZ 155 SEVENTIES POP GENIUS

AVID DISC DAYS

Once more we get you anagramming with more phrases which should lead to five more well-known 70s faces.

QUIZ 153

Q1
'Philadelphia Freedom' was by
c Elton John

Q2
'Portsmouth' was a hit for
b Mike Oldfield

Q3
'Hollywood Nights' was by
a Bob Seger and The Silver Bullet Band

Q4
'Parisienne Walkways' was by
c Gary Moore

Q5
'Tuxedo Junction' was by
b Manhattan Transfer

QUESTION 1 *(5 POINTS)*
Their music might be termed aggressive but this one word band name doesn't deserve to end up here.

DEATH ROOM

QUESTION 2 *(5 POINTS)*
Two words spell out this US ivory tickler.

LOLLY JIBE

QUESTION 3 *(5 POINTS)*
Four words containing all the letters for a four word US group name.

I DRAWN IT FREEHAND

QUESTION 4 *(5 POINTS)*
Find a two-word, much lusted after, pop idol from this three-word description.

AVID DISC DAYS

QUESTION 5 *(5 POINTS)*
Clues aplenty in this apparent phrase of gobbledegook.

SLY BAY HEIRESS

160

SEVENTIES POP GENIUS

DECADE'S END

Cast your mind back to the last few weeks of the 70s.

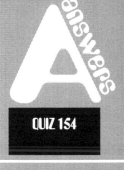

QUESTION 1 *(5 POINTS)*
Who was booed on his Slow Train Coming tour for the effect his new musical direction was taking as a born-again Christian?
a Michael Jackson
b Bob Dylan
c Alice Cooper

QUESTION 2 *(5 POINTS)*
'No More Tears (Enough Is Enough)' was a big hit for Donna Summer dueting with who in December 1979?
a Barbra Streisand
b Neil Diamond
c Amii Stewart

QUESTION 3 *(5 POINTS)*
Ska rules at the close of the 70s, but which of these three charted with 'On My Radio'?
a Madness
b The Specials
c Selecter

QUESTION 4 *(5 POINTS)*
The Boomtown Rats end the decade with a No.13 chart hit called what?
a 'Diamond Lights'
b 'Diamond Fingers'
c 'Diamond Smiles'

QUESTION 5 *(5 POINTS)*
Final 70s No.1, 'Another Brick In The Wall (Part 2)' was written by Pink Floyd's Roger Waters. What does he play in the band?
a Lead guitar
b Keyboards
c Bass guitar

Q1
Just one 70s sighting for
a Pete Wingfield

Q2
The Ruffin in question?
b David Ruffin

Q3
'Don't Leave Me This Way' was a No.13 hit for
b Thelma Houston

Q4
'Snoopy Vs. The Red Baron' was by
b The Hotshots

Q5
'Clog Dance' was a one-off Top 20 hit for
c Violinski

THE 1970 QUIZ

A fresh new decade dawns with Rolf Harris at No.1. Here are five questions based on people who helped shape the 70s' music landscape in the early months.

QUIZ 155

Q1
The anagram revealed is
Motorhead

Q2
The ivory tickler?
Billy Joel

Q3
The US group in question?
Earth Wind And Fire

Q4
Much lusted after, the pop star in question is
David Cassidy

Q5
Clues and gobbledegook reveal
Shirley Bassey

QUESTION 1 *(5 POINTS)*
Led Zeppelin II was the band's first chart-topping album in 1970, but which of these tracks is the only one that appeared on the LP?
a 'Whole Lotta Love'
b 'Dazed And Confused'
c 'Good Times Bad Times'

QUESTION 2 *(6 POINTS)*
The Cuff Links were high in the chart with which of these three singles in January 1970?
a 'Tracy'
b 'Suzanne'
c 'Emily'

QUESTION 3 *(4 POINTS)*
Loosely based on Jack Kerouac's novel On The Road, what film had a Byrds and Steppenwolf sountrack LP that went gold in 1970?
a The Wild Angels
b Easy Rider
c Head

QUESTION 4 *(5 POINTS)*
David Bowie was married in early 1970. Who was his bride on 20 March 1970?
a Angela Cousins
b Angela Wiggington
c Angela Barnett

QUESTION 5 *(5 POINTS)*
Shocking Blue had a February 1970 smash hit with 'Venus'. What nationality were the male / female group?
a Norwegian
b Dutch
c Japanese

JAMAICAN FIVE

A round involving Jamaican musicians who made their mark in the 70s.

QUIZ 158

QUESTION 1 *(5 POINTS)*

'Long Shot Kick De Bucket' was an early-70s chart re-entry for The Pioneers, but what was their biggest hit of the decade?

a 'Give And Take'
b 'Freedom Feeling'
c 'Let Your Yeah Be Yeah'

QUESTION 2 *(5 POINTS)*

In which year did Jamaican duo Althia and Donna top the chart with 'Uptown Top Ranking'?

a 1974
b 1976
c 1978

QUESTION 3 *(5 POINTS)*

Jamaican Ken Boothe had two Trojan Records hits in the mid-70s. 'Everything I Own' went to No.1, but what was his follow-up hit?

a 'Don't You Worry About A Thing'
b 'Crying Over You'
c 'Jamaican Shuffle'

QUESTION 4 *(5 POINTS)*

Which Jamaican artist had much success covering the Cat Stevens song 'Wild World' in 1970?

a Johnny Nash
b Bob Marley
c Jimmy Cliff

QUESTION 5 *(5 POINTS)*

What was the title of Errol Dunkley's 1979 smash hit single?

a 'OK Joe'
b 'OK Fred'
c 'OK Chas'

Q1
The man in
question?
b Bob Dylan

Q2
The duet
partner?
a Barbra Streisand

Q3
'On My Radio'
was a hit for
c Selecter

Q4
The Boomtown
Rats ended the
decade with
c 'Diamond Smiles'

Q5
Roger Waters
plays
c Bass guitar

163

QUIZ 159 SEVENTIES POP GENIUS

TRULY MADLY FALSELY

Simply pick the truth from the lies in these five statements.

Q1
The track in question?
a 'Whole Lotta Love'

QUESTION 1 *(5 POINTS)*
Syreeta's huge hit 'With You I'm Born Again' was as one half of a credited duet with Stevie Wonder.
a True
b False

Q2
The Cuff Links were high in the chart with
a 'Tracy'

QUESTION 2 *(5 POINTS)*
Actor Edward Woodward had a hit with 'The Way You Look Tonight'.
a True
b False

Q3
The rock film in question?
b Easy Rider

QUESTION 3 *(5 POINTS)*
Tammy Wynette's real name is actually Pamela Hickory-Dickens.
a True
b False

Q4
David Bowie's 1970 bride was
c Angela Barnett

QUESTION 4 *(5 POINTS)*
Rolling Stone bass player Bill Wyman released what turned out to be a solo hit album called Armed Gorilla.
a True
b False

Q5
Shocking Blue were
b Dutch

QUESTION 5 *(5 POINTS)*
Paul Young had a 1978 solo hit called simply 'Toast'.
a True
b False

ROCK FAMILY TREES

Five random questions about 70s rock family trees.

QUIZ 158

QUESTION 1 *(5 POINTS)*
Mick Jagger's brother released a solo album long before his illustrious brother. A talent in his own right but what was his name?
a Charlie Greenstock
b Chris Jagger
c Tim Jagger

QUESTION 2 *(5 POINTS)*
Paul McCartney's brother had his own music career, which included a period in chart band Scaffold. Who is he?
a Josh McCartney
b Mike McGear
c Ken McCarthy

QUESTION 3 *(5 POINTS)*
Paul and Linda McCartney's marriage produced three children, Mary (born in 1969), Stella (born in 1971) and who in 1977?
a James McCartney
b Martha McCartney
c Lucy McCartney

QUESTION 4 *(5 POINTS)*
Bob Dylan's youngest son Jakob, by ex-wife Sara, eventually became vocalist and guitarist in which band?
a The Message
b The Red Letter Days
c The Wallflowers

QUESTION 5 *(5 POINTS)*
Which legendary music family were born in Hawthorne, California?
a Childhood home of the Jackson family
b Childhood home of Beach Boys Carl, Brian and Dennis Wilson
c Childhood home of Allman Brothers, Duane and Gregg

Q1
The Pioneers' biggest hit of the decade?
c 'Let Your Yeah Be Yeah'

Q2
'Uptown Top Ranking' topped the chart in
c 1978

Q3
Ken Boothe's follow-up was
b 'Crying Over You'

Q4
'Wild World' was covered by
c Jimmy Cliff

Q5
Errol Dunkley's 1979 smash hit was
b OK Fred'

QUIZ 161 SEVENTIES POP GENIUS

HIDDEN PERSONALITIES

More anagram fun. Hiding their names in crazy phrases are five famous music makers and shakers.

Q1

The truth:
b False: 'With You I'm Born Again' was with Billy Preston

QUESTION 1 *(5 POINTS)*
There's something inside these two words that make another two spelling out a well-known 70s solo star.

BAFFLE IRIS

Q2

The Edward Woodward story was
a True

QUESTION 2 *(5 POINTS)*
More North East than Far East for this two-word act.

RESIST TRIAD

Q3

Tammy real name?
b False: Her real name is Virginia Wynette Pugh

QUESTION 3 *(5 POINTS)*
Who can this mystery man be?

ELDER GYRATOR

Q4

Armed Gorilla?
b False: Wyman's solo album was titled Monkey Grip

QUESTION 4 *(5 POINTS)*
Solo acoustic artist born in 1950.

GOT A MANDARIN JAR

Q5

The truth:
b False: Paul Young sang on the record, but the act name was Streetband

QUESTION 5 *(5 POINTS)*
American voice that first came to our notice in the mid-70s.

ACCLAIMING A PUB

POP'S NEW ORDER

Sweeping changes in pop saw the old order making way for a new, stripped down music model. Here are five questions relating to the dawn of punk.

QUESTION 1 *(5 POINTS)*

US band The Ramones made their live UK debut at which London venue?
a The Roundhouse
b The Rainbow
c The 100 Club

QUESTION 2 *(5 POINTS)*

In 1976, Dr Feelgood played the Kursaal Ballroom in which town?
a Skegness
b Blackpool
c Southend

QUESTION 3 *(5 POINTS)*

Name the single that gave The Clash their chart debut in April 1977.
a 'Clash City Rockers'
b 'Complete Control'
c 'White Riot'

QUESTION 4 *(5 POINTS)*

Promoting early punk was a club in Neal Street, Covent Garden, London, called what?
a The Punk Garden
b The Roxy
c Studio 45

QUESTION 5 *(5 POINTS)*

Malcolm McLaren and ten guests were arrested at an event to promote the Sex Pistols one summer evening in 1977. Where?
a Aboard a River Thames boat trip
b On an aircraft flight returning from Vancouver
c At a reception at the House Of Commons

QUIZ 160

Q1
Mick Jagger's brother?
b Chris Jagger

Q2
Paul McCartney's brother?
b Mike McGear

Q3
Paul and Linda McCartney's third child?
a James McCartney

Q4
Bob Dylan's youngest son Jakob was a member of
c The Wallflowers

Q5
Hawthorne was
b Childhood home of Beach Boys Carl, Brian and Dennis Wilson

167

QUIZ 161

LIFE AFTER THE BEATLES

More questions involving solo Beatle action in the 70s.

Q1

The well-known 70s solo star?

Labi Siffre

QUESTION 1 *(5 POINTS)*

Denny Laine became a long-time associate and band member in Paul McCartney's Wings. What was his previous band?

a Manfred Mann

b The Swinging Blue Jeans

c The Moody Blues

Q2

The act in question?

Dire Straits

QUESTION 2 *(5 POINTS)*

John Lennon turned producer for an album titled Pussy Cats in 1974. Who was the artist and friend involved?

a Nilsson

b Ringo Starr

c Keith Moon

Q3

The mystery man?

Roger Daltrey

QUESTION 3 *(5 POINTS)*

Sentimental Journey was Ringo's first solo album. What appeared on the cover?

a The local pub where he grew up in Liverpool

b A family photo album

c Milk bottles on a garden wall

Q4

The solo acoustic artist born in 1950?

Joan Armatrading

QUESTION 4 *(5 POINTS)*

George Harrison's 'My Sweet Lord' was the subject of a lawsuit involving which 1963 hit? Name the song and the act.

a 'Dancing In The Street' by Martha and The Vandellas

b 'He's So Fine' by The Chiffons

c 'Da Doo Ron Ron' by The Crystals

Q5

The voice and the man?

Paul Gambaccini

QUESTION 5 *(5 POINTS)*

Paul McCartney and Wings enjoyed three No.1 albums in the 70s. Ram and Band On The Run were two. Which was the third?

a London Town

b Back To The Egg

c Venus And Mars

SEVENTIES POP GENIUS QUIZ 164

ONE FROM THREE

Scan the three singles and simply name the artist in question for 25 easy points.

QUESTION 1 *(5 POINTS)*
Who was responsible for...
'I'm Gonna Love You Just A Little More Baby'
'Never Never Gonna Give Ya Up'
'Can't Get Enough Of Your Love, Babe'

QUESTION 2 *(5 POINTS)*
Who had these early-70s hits?
'My Baby Loves Lovin''
'Julie Do Ya Love Me'
'When You Are A King'

QUESTION 3 *(5 POINTS)*
Whose three are these?
'Let The Music Play'
'You See The Trouble with Me'
'Baby, We Better Try To Get It Together'

QUESTION 4 *(5 POINTS)*
Who's this?
'Teenage Rampage'
'The Six Teens'
'Fox On The Run'

QUESTION 5 *(5 POINTS)*
Three clues: name the group.
'Heaven Must Be Missing An Angel'
'Don't Take Away The Music'
'Whodunit'

QUIZ 162

Q1
The Ramones made their live debut at
a The Roundhouse

Q2
Dr Feelgood played the Kursaal Ballroom in
c Southend

Q3
The Clash chart debut?
c 'White Riot'

Q4
The Covent Garden club was
b The Roxy

Q5
The unusual Sex Pistols venue?
a Aboard a River Thames boat trip

169

QUIZ 163

Q1
Denny Laine was a former member of
c The Moody Blues

Q2
The artist and friend in question?
a Nilsson

Q3
Ringo's cover featured
a The local pub where he grew up in Liverpool

Q4
The subject of a lawsuit?
b 'He's So Fine' by The Chiffons

Q5
The third No.1 album by Paul McCartney and Wings?
c Venus And Mars

SEVENTIES POP GENIUS  QUIZ 164

INTRODUCING... FOR THE VERY FIRST TIME

Making their first tentative steps on planet rock in the late 70s...

QUIZ 164

QUESTION 1 *(5 POINTS)*

On 5th May 1979 this act arrived on the scene with its first chart entry – the album A Life In The Day. Who were they?

a The Doobie Brothers

b Simple Minds

c Simply Red

Q1
The man responsible?
Barry White

QUESTION 2 *(5 POINTS)*

Their 1979 chart debut came courtesy of 'The Sound Of The Suburbs'.

a The Members

b The Merton Parkas

c The Maytals

Q2
The three hits were all by
White Plains

QUESTION 3 *(5 POINTS)*

This band introduced themselves at the end of the decade with the single 'Money'.

a Liquid Gold

b Love Unlimited

c The Flying Lizards

Q3
Three hits, all from the substantial body of work that was
Barry White - again!

QUESTION 4 *(5 POINTS)*

They came, they saw, they conquered and then vanished from the chart. Their fine legacy was 'Driver's Seat'.

a Stretch

b Sniff 'N' The Tears

c The Cars

Q4
'Teenage Rampage', 'The Six Teens', 'Fox On The Run'?
Sweet

QUESTION 5 *(5 POINTS)*

This group introduced themselves to the world with 'Gangsters' in the summer of 79.

a The Special A.K.A.

b Madness

c The Beat

Q5
The group in question?
Tavares

SINGER IN THE BAND

Five straight answers to five straight questions with no alternatives: who were the lead singers in these five 70s bands?

QUIZ 165

Q1
The album Jazz was by
Queen

Q2
R. Dean Taylor's 1974 hit was
'There's A Ghost In My House'

Q3
New member of The Rolling Stones in 1976?
Ronnie Wood

Q4
The female solo singer is
Carly Simon

Q5
Roger **Taylor**, R. Dean **Taylor**, Ronnie Wood replaced Mick **Taylor**, Carly Simon wed James **Taylor**

QUESTION 1 *(4 POINTS)*
Who was the bass-playing lead singer in Thin Lizzy?

QUESTION 2 *(5 POINTS)*
Who was the guitar-toting lead singer in Ten Years After?

QUESTION 3 *(5 POINTS)*
Who sang lead vocals in Mott The Hoople?

QUESTION 4 *(5 POINTS)*
Who fronted anglo-American rock outfit Foreigner?

QUESTION 5 *(6 POINTS)*
Who was The Chairmen Of The Board's lead vocalist?

SEVENTIES POP GENIUS QUIZ 168

CASH FOR QUESTIONS

No money will actually change hands for this run of questions testing you on Johnny Cash, whose most successful chart hit decade was the 70s, but there is the satisfaction of gathering another 25 points.

QUESTION 1 *(5 POINTS)*

Who wrote Johnny Cash's biggest UK hit, 'A Boy Named Sue'?
a Shel Silverstein
b Jim Steinman
c Hank Williams

QUESTION 2 *(5 POINTS)*

What was the title of Johnny Cash's last hit album of the 70s?
a Itchy Feet
b Itchy Fingers
c Itchy Throat

QUESTION 3 *(6 POINTS)*

In which year was the boy named J.R. Cash born?
a 1922
b 1932
c 1942

QUESTION 4 *(4 POINTS)*

A 21st century movie starring Joaquin Phoenix as Johnny Cash was called what?
a Walk Tall
b The Man In Black
c Walk The Line

QUESTION 5 *(5 POINTS)*

Aside from his habit of wearing an all-black outfit on stage, which other fashion item is associated with Johnny Cash.
a A rhinestone encrusted Stetson
b A bronze, silver and gold-patched guitar strap
c A long three-quarter length coat

Q1
Arriving on the scene were
b Simple Minds

Q2
Debuting in 1979 were
a The Members

Q3
Introducing themselves were
c The Flying Lizards

Q4
'Driver's Seat'
b Sniff 'N' The Tears

Q5
Introducing themselves in the summer of 79?
a The Special A.K.A.

QUIZ 167

Q1
The Thin Lizzy man in question?
Phil Lynott

Q2
The guitar-toting lead singer in Ten Years After?
Alvin Lee

Q3
Lead vocals in Mott The Hoople?
Ian Hunter

Q4
Fronting anglo-American rock outfit Foreigner?
Mick Jones

Q5
Chairmen Of The Board's lead vocalist?
General Norman Johnson

WARNING: APPROACH WITH CAUTION

A round devoted to worthy but nevertheless obscure music types

QUESTION 1 *(5 POINTS)*

The quaintly-named Candlewick Green posted just one hit in the 70s and that at No.21. A pop radio favourite, what was the title?
a 'Who Do You Think You Are?'
b 'Funky Moped'
c 'Put Yourself In My Place'

QUESTION 2 *(5 POINTS)*

Which legendary blues musician led the 70s band C.C.S., whose highest chart hit came with 'Tap Turns On The Water'?
a Eric Burdon
b Jack Bruce
c Alexis Korner

QUESTION 3 *(5 POINTS)*

The US musician J.J. Cale had a series of hit albums starting in the 70s. What did the "J.J." stand for?
a Jon Joe
b Jean Jacques
c Just Jack

QUESTION 4 *(5 POINTS)*

What was unusual about singer-songwriter Jackson Browne's only UK 70s hit single?
a It was a cover version
b It was also released by Jackson Brown (without an "e") in the same week
c The single was the first to register in the UK chart without a title

QUESTION 5 *(5 POINTS)*

The Band Of The Black Watch hit single 'Dance Of The Cuckoos' was better known as what?
a The tune used for the 70s BBC TV News broadcasts
b The closing piece from Benjamin Britten's opera Peter Grimes
c The 'Laurel And Hardy' Theme

174

IN THE BEST POSSIBLE TASTE

Test your knowledge on music champion, DJ and comic Kenny Everett.

QUIZ 168

QUESTION 1 *(5 POINTS)*
Kenny Everett's real name was what?
a Maurice Cole
b Norman Green
c Arthur James

QUESTION 2 *(5 POINTS)*
'Captain Kremmen (Retribution)' was the title of Everett's only 70s hit. Who is jointly credited on the record?
a Dave Cash
b Mike Vickers
c Freddie Mercury

QUESTION 3 *(5 POINTS)*
What was the name of the innovative new TV show fronted by Kenny Everett on Thames TV in 1978?
a The Captain Kremmen TV Comic
b The Kenny Everett Video Show
c The Sid Snot Hour

QUESTION 4 *(5 POINTS)*
Everett was also 'the voice' behind TV public information films. What was the cartoon character called who he voiced?
a Marcel Mouse
b Charley the cat
c Sir Hissington Snake

QUESTION 5 *(5 POINTS)*
In which year did Kenny Everett die?
a 1995
b 1999
c 2003

Q1
The man who wrote 'A Boy Named Sue'?
a Shel Silverstein

Q2
Johnny Cash's last hit album of the 70s?
a Itchy Feet

Q3
J.R. Cash was born in
b 1932

Q4
The 21st century movie starring Joaquin Phoenix was
c Walk The Line

Q5
That 'other' Cash fashion item?
c A long three-quarter length coat

answers

QUIZ 169

NEW YORK GROOVE

The city so good they named it twice gets five brain-teasing questions beginning with one about the quiz title itself.

Q1
The Candlewick Green pop radio favourite?
a 'Who Do You Think You Are'

Q2
The legendary blues musician was
c Alexis Korner

Q3
"J.J." stands for
b Jean Jacques

Q4
Jackson Browne's only UK 70s hit single?
a It was a cover version ('Stay')

Q5
'Dance Of The Cuckoos' was better known as
c The 'Laurel And Hardy' Theme

QUESTION 1 *(5 POINTS)*
Who had a hit with 'New York Groove' in late 1975?
a Paper Lace
b The Rubettes
c Hello

QUESTION 2 *(4 POINTS)*
'Native New Yorker' was a smash hit for which of these three?
a Gloria Gaynor
b Odyssey
c Crystal Gayle

QUESTION 3 *(6 POINTS)*
What was the correct title of the New York name-checking hit for T. Rex?
a 'New York City'
b 'New York Town'
c 'New York State Of Mind'

QUESTION 4 *(5 POINTS)*
'New York, New York' was the single. Who was the man that named the city twice in 1978?
a Frank Sinatra
b Gerard Kenny
c Lou Reed

QUESTION 5 *(5 POINTS)*
On the Genesis album The Lamb Lies Down On Broadway, what's the correct title of the track that name-checks the 'Big Apple'?
a 'I'm Flying Into NY'
b 'The Streets Of New York'
c 'Back In N.Y.C.'

SEVENTIES POP GENIUS QUIZ 172

WORD UP

Five titles missing one thing. Select the correct title on offer and 25 easy points will be yours.

QUIZ 170

QUESTION 1 *(5 POINTS)*
Thin Lizzy's 1978 album release was a 62-week chart limpet but what was it called? _____ And Dangerous.
a Live And Dangerous
b Back And Dangerous
c Hot And Dangerous

QUESTION 2 *(6 POINTS)*
US vocalist Mary MacGregor's 1977 smash hit single was titled what? _____ Between Two Lovers.
a 'Torn Between Two Lovers'
b 'Caught Between Two Lovers'
c 'Lost Between Two Lovers'

QUESTION 3 *(6 POINTS)*
'Something That I _____' was a 1979 chart hit for The Ruts.
a 'Something That I Want'
b 'Something That I Said'
c 'Something That I Did'

QUESTION 4 *(3 POINTS)*
Life Is A_____ 10cc compared life to which of these?
a 'Life Is A Lasagne'
b 'Life Is A Trifle'
c 'Life Is A Minestrone'

QUESTION 5 *(5 POINTS)*
'I Get The _____ Feeling' needs a gap filling for Jackie Wilson's 70s classic.
a 'I Get The Greatest Feeling'
b 'I Get The Sweetest Feeling'
c 'I Get The Strangest Feeling'

Q1
Kenny Everett's real name was
a Maurice Cole

Q2
Jointly credited on the only Kenny Everett 70s hit?
b Mike Vickers

Q3
The innovative new TV show?
b The Kenny Everett Video Show

Q4
The cartoon character?
b Charley the cat

Q5
Kenny Everett died in
a 1995

177

DO YOU AGREE?

That's for you to decide when answering five more true or false conundrums connected to album releases.

QUIZ 171

Q1
'New York Groove' was a late 1975 hit for
c Hello

Q2
'Native New Yorker' was a smash hit for
b Odyssey

Q3
The correct title of the New York name-checking hit for T. Rex?
a 'New York City'

Q4
'New York, New York' was named twice in 1978 by
b Gerard Kenny

Q5
The Genesis track in question?
c 'Back In N.Y.C.'

QUESTION 1 *(5 POINTS)*
Long gone legendary blues musician Robert Johnson registered two UK No.1 albums in the 70s.
a True
b False

QUESTION 2 *(4 POINTS)*
The Who had a hit album titled Odds And Sods.
a True
b False

QUESTION 3 *(6 POINTS)*
Matching Tie & Handkerchief was a minor hit album for Ian Dury And The Blockheads.
a True
b False

QUESTION 4 *(5 POINTS)*
Paul McCartney and Wings' album Band On The Run was released on the Apple label.
a True
b False

QUESTION 5 *(5 POINTS)*
Fifty-something country Star Slim Whitman had two UK chart-topping albums in the 70s?
a True
b False

I'VE HAD CONSIDERABLY MORE HITS THAN YOU!

Chart-topping hit singles: pick the winner in each case.

QUIZ 172

QUESTION 1 *(4 POINTS)*
Six 70s chart-topping singles is the achievement peak, but which of these three is the correct choice?
a The Police
b Slade
c Gary Numan

QUESTION 2 *(5 POINTS)*
Three 70s No.1s is the best tally for which of these solo stars?
a Diana Ross
b Suzi Quatro
c Gary Glitter

QUESTION 3 *(4 POINTS)*
An amazing seven UK 70s chart-toppers is the winning total for one of this trio of acts.
a Abba
b The Osmonds
c Elvis Presley

QUESTION 4 *(5 POINTS)*
Just two No.1s wins this time. Who trumps the other two acts in this line-up?
a Benny Hill
b Elton John
c Bee Gees

QUESTION 5 *(7 POINTS)*
Five is the impressive haul of chart-toppers achieved in the 70s by one from these three.
a T. Rex
b Rod Stewart
c Mud

Q1
Thin Lizzy's 1978 chart limpet was
a Live And Dangerous

Q2
Mary MacGregor's 1977 smash was
a 'Torn Between Two Lovers'

Q3
The 1979 chart hit for The Ruts was
b 'Something That I Said'

Q4
10cc believed
c 'Life Is A Minestrone'

Q5
Jackie Wilson's 70s classic?
b 'I Get The Sweetest Feeling'

TERRACE TUNES

OK, this round is more about football, but if you bought any of these records it probably wasn't for the critically-acclaimed music quality!

QUIZ 173

Q1
Blues musician
Robert Johnson
registering two
UK No.1 albums?
b False

Q2
Odds And Sods
by The Who is
a True

Q3
Matching Tie &
Hankerchief?
b False: It was a
minor hit LP for
Monty Python

Q4
Band On The
Run on the Apple
label?
a True

Q5
Slim Whitman had
two UK chart-
topping albums in
the 70s?
a True

QUESTION 1 *(5 POINTS)*
A hit for Cockney Rejects, 'I'm Forever Blowing Bubbles' was a bigger chart hit for the West Ham United Cup Squad. Name the year.
a FA Cup Final 1973
b FA Cup Final 1974
c FA Cup Final 1975

QUESTION 2 *(5 POINTS)*
Leeds were to football what Elton John was to the 70s charts: all-conquering. They secured a Top 10 hit with which of these three?
a 'Marching With Revie's Army'
b 'Leeds United'
c 'The Boys In White Are United'

QUESTION 3 *(5 POINTS)*
England World Cup chart-topper 'Back Home' was recorded when England were world champions. Who wrote and produced the song?
a Mickie Most and Alexis Korner
b Bill Martin and Phil Coulter
c Lonnie Donegan and Chas McDevitt

QUESTION 4 *(5 POINTS)*
'We'll Be With You' sang The Potters in 1972, but which set of fans recorded this ahead of their team's Football League Cup win?
a Stoke City
b Arsenal
c Wolverhampton Wanderers

QUESTION 5 *(5 POINTS)*
'Y Viva Espana' was the inspiration for Fulham fans' Tony Rees and The Cottagers 'Viva El Fulham' in 1975. Who sang the earlier version?
a Cynthia
b Sandie
c Sylvia

GOING SOLO

Five questions about rock and pop superstars who decided to leave the comfort of their bands and brothers to do their own thing.

QUIZ 174

QUESTION 1 *(5 POINTS)*
Pink Floyd's David Gilmour made his solo chart debut with which album title?
a David Gilmour
b About Face
c Honest Mistake

QUESTION 2 *(6 POINTS)*
Which Gibb brother was responsible for the hit album Shadow Dancing?
a Barry Gibb
b Robin Gibb
c Andy Gibb

QUESTION 3 *(4 POINTS)*
Rod Stewart's first hit album as a solo artist was which of these three?
a Sing It Again Rod
b Gasoline Alley
c Every Picture Tells A Story

QUESTION 4 *(5 POINTS)*
Which of these three first entered the singles chart as a solo artist in 1970 with 'Love The One You're With'?
a David Crosby
b Graham Nash
c Stephen Stills

QUESTION 5 *(5 POINTS)*
Diana Ross's solo career began in 1970 with which UK hit single?
a 'Love Child'
b 'Reach Out And Touch'
c 'You Are Everything'

Q1
Six No.1s: the correct choice?
b Slade

Q2
Three 70s No.1s is the best tally for
c Gary Glitter

Q3
Seven UK 70s chart-toppers is the winning total for
a Abba

Q4
Trumping the other two acts in this line-up?
c Bee Gees

Q5
Five chart-toppers was achieved by
b Rod Stewart

181

A COOL RECIPE

Five more anagrams like this one to untangle from the sometimes cryptic clues.

QUIZ 175

Q1
**West Ham
v Fulham at
Wembley?**
c FA Cup Final
1975

Q2
**The imaginative
anthem title?**
b 'Leeds United'

Q3
**'Back Home'
was written and
produced by?**
b Bill Martin and Phil
Coulter

Q4
**Hit makers The
Potters were the
fans of**
a Stoke City

Q5
**The singer of the
monster summer
anthem?**
c Sylvia

QUESTION 1 *(3 POINTS)*
**Possibly the easiest anagram in the book, so do not fail to
identify this two-word legend.**

RID ME HI JINX

QUESTION 2 *(5 POINTS)*
Snakes alive! Two words please.

A COOL RECIPE

QUESTION 3 *(6 POINTS)*
Mum's the word for this two-word 70s outfit.

GENUINE POTENTIAL

QUESTION 4 *(4 POINTS)*
Two-word vocalist with two UK No.1 albums in the 70s.

O MERRY COP

QUESTION 5 *(7 POINTS)*
A truly American solo star. Two words required.

EDITORIAL COG

REAL OR BOGUS

Quite a bit of guesswork required probably, but which of these five
bizarrely-named 70s acts are real and which are complete fabrications?

QUIZ 178

QUESTION 1 *(5 POINTS)*
**Real or bogus: Lori and The Chameleons had a minor hit on the
Sire label in 1979.**
a Real
b Bogus

Q1
**David Gilmour's
debut album
title?**
a David Gilmour

QUESTION 2 *(5 POINTS)*
**Can it really be true that one Pluto Shervington hit the Top 10 in
1976?**
a Real
b Bogus

Q2
**Shadow Dancing
was by**
c Andy Gibb

QUESTION 3 *(5 POINTS)*
**A band of hit-makers called Excrement? Surely even punks
wouldn't stoop so low!**
a Real
b Bogus

Q3
**Rod Stewart's
first hit album as
a solo artist was**
b Gasoline Alley

QUESTION 4 *(5 POINTS)*
**Would any band consider naming themselves Boogie Oogie
Oogie?**
a Real
b Bogus

Q4
**Entering the
singles chart with
'Love The One
You're With'?**
c Stephen Stills

QUESTION 5 *(5 POINTS)*
**'The Great Escape' was the work of 70s hit-makers We Are
Scientists: real or bogus?**
a Real
b Bogus

Q5
**Diana Ross's solo
career began in
1970 with**
b 'Reach Out And
Touch'

183

answers

Q1
The two-word legend?
Jimi Hendrix

Q2
Snakes alive! It must be
Alice Cooper

Q3
The group in question?
Lieutenant Pigeon

Q4
The man in question?
Perry Como

Q5
The American solo star?
Rita Coolidge

QUIZ 179 SEVENTIES POP GENIUS

THE GREATEST HITS DECADE

Just select the correct titles of these massive unit-shifting LPs.

QUESTION 1 *(5 POINTS)*
The Beach Boys enjoyed 10 weeks atop the chart with this summer offering.
a 40 Greatest Hits
b All Summer Long
c 20 Golden Greats

QUESTION 2 *(5 POINTS)*
Various acts contributed in various volumes of this No.1 70s success story.
a Motown Classics
b Motown Chartbusters
c Motown Monster Hits

QUESTION 3 *(5 POINTS)*
Dominating the mid-70s was a best of the Carpenters LP. Which title rings true?
a Richard And Karen's Top 20
b The Singles 1969-1973
c Old, New, Borrowed And Blue

QUESTION 4 *(5 POINTS)*
Abba swiftly repackaged their best work in 1976. What was the album called?
a Abba – Solid Gold
b Gold – Greatest Hits
c Greatest Hits

QUESTION 5 *(5 POINTS)*
In 1979 which of these disco LPs was No.1 for six weeks between studio offerings from Tubeway Army and Led Zeppelin?
a Disco Fever
b The Best Disco Album In The World
c 40 Big Disco Floor Fillers

SEVENTIES POP GENIUS QUIZ 180

ONE-TIMERS

A selection of one hit wonders with the artists missing. Select the correct act every time and 25 points will be yours.

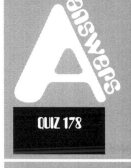

QUIZ 178

QUESTION 1 *(5 POINTS)*
Who was responsible for the very groovy 'Groovin' With Mr Bloe' in 1970?
a Mr Bloe
b Booker T and The MG's
c Donovan

QUESTION 2 *(6 POINTS)*
Match up the correct US male vocalist who hit just the once with 'It's Better To Have (And Don't Need)'.
a Don Covay
b Les Crane
c Bobby Fuller

QUESTION 3 *(5 POINTS)*
'Black Pearl' was the solitary hit for which of these three?
a Horace Faith
b Joe Fagin
c Inez Foxx

QUESTION 4 *(4 POINTS)*
'You Just Might See Me Cry' was a massive hit for who?
a Aled Jones
b Our Kid
c Neil Reid

QUESTION 5 *(5 POINTS)*
The TV theme to Owen MD was a Top 10 single better known as 'Sleepy Shores'. Who was responsible?
a Simon Park Orchestra
b Mr Acker Bilk
c Johnny Pearson Orchestra

QUIZ 178

Q1
Lori and The Chameleons had a minor hit on the Sire label in 1979.
a Real

Q2
Pluto Shervington hit the Top 10 in 1976.
a Real

Q3
A band of hit-makers called Excrement?
b Bogus

Q4
A band called Boogie Oogie Oogie?
b Bogus

Q5
We Are Scientists ere a noughties band
b Bogus

Q1
The Beach Boys enjoyed 10 weeks at the top with
c 20 Golden Greats

Q2
The No.1 70s success story?
b Motown Chartbusters

Q3
The correct Carpenters LP title?
b The Singles 1969-1973

Q4
Abba's swiftly repackaged offering was called
c Greatest Hits

Q5
No.1 for six weeks was
b The Best Disco Album In The World

QUIZ 181 SEVENTIES POP GENIUS

THE FIRST CUT IS THE DEEPEST

Earliest signs of life from five acts announcing their arrival in the 70s.

QUESTION 1 *(5 POINTS)*
'Reunited' is the smash hit most associated with Peaches and Herb but can you name their chart debut three months earlier?
a 'Remember'
b 'All Night Celebration'
c 'Shake Your Groove Thing'

QUESTION 2 *(5 POINTS)*
Tom Petty and The Heartbreakers' 'American Girl' has stood the test of time better, but their debut UK single was higher placed. Name it.
a 'Don't Come Around Here No More'
b 'Anything That's Rock 'N' Roll'
c 'Learning To Fly'

QUESTION 3 *(5 POINTS)*
'Time For Action' was their first and highest-placed single. Which group made their chart debut with this rousing single in 1979?
a Secret Love Machines
b Secret Affair
c Sound Of London

QUESTION 4 *(5 POINTS)*
Sparks made their first spectacular mark on the UK singles chart with 'This Town Ain't Big Enough For Both Of Us' in which year?
a 1972
b 1974
c 1976

QUESTION 5 *(5 POINTS)*
Squeeze took a year to break the Top 10 with 'Cool For Cats', but what was their 1978 debut hit?
a 'Slap & Tickle'
b 'Another Nail In My Heart'
c 'Take Me I'm Yours'

SEVENTIES POP GENIUS ■ QUIZ 182

COVER VERSIONS

25 points at stake for correctly identifying facts about some key 7os cover versions.

QUESTION 1 *(5 POINTS)*

Prelude turned 'After The Gold Rush' into a chart hit - their cover of an album track written and recorded by who?
a Pete Seeger
b Pete Townshend
c Neil Young

Q1
'Groovin' With Mr Bloe' was by
a Mr Bloe

QUESTION 2 *(5 POINTS)*

Whose cover of The Rolling Stones' 'Ruby Tuesday' gave the song its first appearance in the UK chart in 1970?
a Marianne Faithfull
b Buffy Sainte-Marie
c Melanie

Q2
The US male vocalist in question?
a Don Covay

QUESTION 3 *(5 POINTS)*

'She's Not There' was a hit for The Zombies written by the band's Rod Argent. Which of these acts did NOT have a hit cover version?
a UK Subs
b Echo and The Bunnymen
c Santana

Q3
'Black Pearl' was the solitary hit for
a Horace Faith

QUESTION 4 *(6 POINTS)*

Eddie Cochran's 'Summertime Blues' has been covered by all three below, but only one managed to hit the singles chart with it.
a The Who
b Olivia Newton-John
c The Clash

Q4
'You Just Might See Me Cry' was a massive hit for
b Our Kid

QUESTION 5 *(4 POINTS)*

Which of these covers did Bryan Ferry make the Top 10 with to kick-off his solo career in 1973?
a 'You Go To My Head' written by J. Fred Coots and Haven Gillespie
b 'Smoke Gets In Your Eyes' written by Jerome Kern and Otto Harbach
c 'A Hard Rain's A-Gonna Fall' written by Bob Dylan

Q5
The TV theme to Owen MD was by
c Johnny Pearson Orchestra

QUIZ 181

TV THEMES

Five TV theme tune-related questions from the golden era.

Q1

The Peaches and Herb chart debut?

c 'Shake Your Groove Thing'

QUESTION 1 *(6 POINTS)*

The Happy Days theme tune was a UK hit in 1977 courtesy of which of these acts?

a Jan and Dean with Peter Tork
b Pratt and McClain with Brotherlove
c Sha Na Na with Mike Post

Q2

Tom Petty and The Heartbreakers' debut was

b 'Anything That's Rock 'N' Roll'

QUESTION 2 *(4 POINTS)*

The US show Chico And The Man had a theme written and performed by who?

a Jose Feliciano
b John Denver
c Micky Dolenz

Q3

'Time For Action' was the introductory hit by

b Secret Affair

QUESTION 3 *(5 POINTS)*

The Monty Python TV series theme tune was nabbed copyright free from which famous marching tune?

a 'The Liberty Bell'
b 'Carnival Of The Animals'
c 'Colonel Bogey'

Q4

The Sparks debut was in

b 1974

QUESTION 4 *(5 POINTS)*

Which group enjoyed a UK No.7 hit with their version of the Banana Splits TV theme called 'Banana Splits (The Tra La La Song)'?

a Dimestars
b The Dweebs
c The Dickies

Q5

Squeeze made their debut with

c 'Take Me I'm Yours'

QUESTION 5 *(5 POINTS)*

'Whatever Happened To You', theme to TV's Whatever Happened To The Likely Lads?, was co-written and sung by who?

a Manfred Mann
b Mike Hugg
c Mike D'Abo

SEVENTIES POP GENIUS QUIZ 184

HIGHER OR LOWER?

Straightforward enough: all you have to do is guess (unless of course you are a true genius and know!) which of these two 70s classic singles charted highest.

QUESTION 1 *(5 POINTS)*
First up: 'Jet' by Paul McCartney and Wings. Higher or lower than the same group's 'With A Little Luck'?

QUESTION 2 *(5 POINTS)*
'Street Fighting Man': higher or lower than The Rolling Stones' next hit 'Tumbling Dice'?

QUESTION 3 *(5 POINTS)*
'Candle In The Wind': is it higher or lower than Elton John's version of The Who's 'Pinball Wizard'?

QUESTION 4 *(5 POINTS)*
'If You Leave Me Now': is it higher or lower than Chicago's other major 70s hit '25 Or 6 To 4'?

QUESTION 5 *(5 POINTS)*
Finally, two Status Quo singles. 'Paper Plane': is it higher or lower than later release 'Whatever You Want'?

QUIZ 182

Q1
Prelude's chart hit was written by
c Neil Young

Q2
The 'Ruby Tuesday' cover was by
c Melanie

Q3
'She's Not There' was not a hit for
b Echo and The Bunnymen

Q4
Charting with 'Summertime Blues' were
a The Who

Q5
Bryan Ferry's debut?
c Bob Dylan's 'A Hard Rain's A-Gonna Fall'

QUIZ 183

SLIMY ACORNS AND CANNY RATS

Slimy Acorn is just one of five more rock 'n' roll anagrams to solve.

Q1
The Happy Days theme tune?
b Pratt and McClain with Brotherlove

Q2
The Chico And The Man theme tune?
a Jose Feliciano

Q3
The Monty Python TV theme tune was nabbed from
a 'The Liberty Bell'

Q4
Enjoying a hit with their cover of the Banana Splits TV theme?
c The Dickies

Q5
The co-writer and singer in question
b Mike Hugg

QUESTION 1 *(5 POINTS)*
Female solo star with a male name.

SLIMY ACORN

QUESTION 2 *(5 POINTS)*
Two-word US artist with a hard act to live up to.

AS IN CANNY RAT

QUESTION 3 *(5 POINTS)*
A much revered soul man.

CERTIFY DUALISM

QUESTION 4 *(5 POINTS)*
Singer-songwriter with three 70s hit albums to his credit.

RODEO CHANNEL

QUESTION 5 *(5 POINTS)*
Two-word band name with a double transport connection between anagram and answer.

MATURE BYWAY

SEVENTIES POP GENIUS | QUIZ 184

FIVE OF THE BEST

Or, to be more precise, five questions connected to the five best-selling singles released in the 70s.

QUIZ 184

QUESTION 1 *(4 POINTS)*

Boney M's 'Rivers Of Babylon' / 'Brown Girl In The Ring' and 'Mary's Boy Child – Oh My Lord' are both in the decade's Top 5 best-seller list. What nationality was the group's producer Frank Farian?

Q1
Higher or lower?
LOWER: 'Jet' reached No.7 while 'With A Little Luck' peaked at No.5

QUESTION 2 *(5 POINTS)*

With all-time sales of more than two million, 'Bohemian Rhapsody' is the best-selling single released in the 70s, but a large proportion of its sales came many years after its 1975 release. In which year did it return to the top of the chart?

Q2
Higher or lower?
LOWER: 'Street Fighting Man' made 21 while 'Tumbling Dice' hit No.5.

QUESTION 3 *(5 POINTS)*

Boney M again. Which of their two songs in the 70s top five best-sellers list (see Question 1) was the bigger hit?

Q3
Higher or lower?
LOWER: 'Candle In The Wind' peaked at No.11 while 'Pinball Wizard' hit No.7.

QUESTION 4 *(5 POINTS)*

Australian John Farrar wrote and produced another of our Top 5 70s singles, 'You're The One That I Want' for John Travolta and Olivia Newton-John. Which hugely successful British group did Farrar join in the 70s?

Q4
Higher or lower?
HIGHER: 'If You Leave Me Now' was a No.1 while '25 Or 6 To 4' made No.7.

QUESTION 5 *(6 POINTS)*

Finally, 'Mull Of Kintyre': Paul McCartney and Wings created what would, for a period, become Britain's best-selling single during the time they spent recording which album?

Q5
Higher or lower?
LOWER: 'Paper Plane' made No.8 but 'Whatever You Want' peaked at No.4.

191

QUIZ 187 SEVENTIES POP GENIUS

ALBUM ART DETECTIVE

Another picture quiz where you need to turn art detective and identify these five album titles and artists from the cover, which we have printed without the title and artist name.

Q1
The female star with a male name?
Carly Simon

QUESTION 1 *(4 POINTS)*
The act and the album title required for the points on this 1974 release that charted for 19 weeks.

Q2
The artist with a hard act to live up to?
Nancy Sinatra

QUESTION 2 *(6 POINTS)*
Give the correct album and act name that appeared at the top and bottom of the sleeve pictured.

Q3
The much revered soul man?
Curtis Mayfield

QUESTION 3 *(5 POINTS)*
An album that helped cement the future success of an act not stuck in the Sixties.

Q4
The hit singer-songwriter?
Leonard Cohen

QUESTION 4 *(5 POINTS)*
Which album and act packaged a 1975 release with this fantasy landscape?

Q5
The two-word band name?
Tubeway Army

QUESTION 5 *(5 POINTS)*
Surely enough clues on this cover to nail this artist and album title.

A YEAR'S TOP ALBUMS

An all-album round restricted to a bizarre mixture of No.1 albums from one year in the decade – a year which is the answer to the fifth and final question.

QUIZ 186

QUESTION 1 *(5 POINTS)*
Famous for his 'Play In A Day' manual, King Size Guitar was his only other hit album before topping the LP chart with 22 Golden Guitar Greats in the 70s. Identify the guitarist.

Q1
Frank Farian's nationality?
German

QUESTION 2 *(5 POINTS)*
Guitars to the fore again. Can you identify the group from the No.1 album title Blue For You?

Q2
'Bohemian Rhapsody' returned to the top in
1991

QUESTION 3 *(5 POINTS)*
Charlotte Cornwell, Julie Covington and Rula Lenska were the trio who put this TV soundtrack release atop the album chart. Name this release.

Q3
The bigger hit?
'Rivers Of Babylon' / 'Brown Girl In The Ring', selling 1,985,000

QUESTION 4 *(5 POINTS)*
Name the budget record label which enjoyed chart-topping action in this mystery year with a Greatest Hits release for Perry Como and a various artists compilation titled Soul Motion.

Q4
John Farrar joined
The Shadows

QUESTION 5 *(5 POINTS)*
Which year have all four previous questions been based on?

Q5
The album in question?
London Town

QUIZ 187

I'M THE DRUMMER

Five questions to uncover the bands these five drummers beat out rhythms for.

QUESTION 1 *(3 POINTS)*
Who has banged the skins down the decades for Fleetwood Mac?
a Lindsey Buckingham
b Mick Fleetwood
c John McVie

QUESTION 2 *(5 POINTS)*
Drummer Phil Collins filled the void left by vocalist Peter Gabriel in Genesis. Who helped out on drums once this happened?
a Chester Thompson
b Mel Gaynor
c Brian Tichy

QUESTION 3 *(5 POINTS)*
Which of these three bands did Kenney Jones never play and record with?
a The Who
b The Faces
c Humble Pie

QUESTION 4 *(7 POINTS)*
Who was the drummer named on the front cover of album Déjà Vu alongside Crosby, Stills, Nash and Young?
a Dallas Taylor
b Greg Reeves
c John Sebastian

QUESTION 5 *(5 POINTS)*
What nationality is AC/DC's 70s drummer Phil Rudd?
a Australian
b New Zealander
c Scottish

SEVENTIES POP GENIUS QUIZ 190

THEME SONG HEAVEN (OR HELL)

Another wave of cinematic and TV nostalgia with 25 points to play for.

QUESTION 1 *(4 POINTS)*
'Good Ol' Boys' was the theme tune sung by Waylon Jennings to which hugely popular TV show?

QUESTION 2 *(5 POINTS)*
'Something Tells Me (Something Is Gonna Happen Tonight)' was the theme tune to whose 70s show?

QUESTION 3 *(6 POINTS)*
The Rockford Files theme tune was the first of many massively successful compositions for which US composer / songwriter.

QUESTION 4 *(5 POINTS)*
Whose 'Theme From 'The Deer Hunter' (Cavatina)' went Top 10 in 1979?

QUESTION 5 *(5 POINTS)*
Although credited as being by The Muppets, Kermit The Frog's nephew Robin (actually Jerry Nelson) is the vocalist on which 1977 Top 10 hit?

Q1
The 'Play In A Day' man?
Bert Weedon

Q2
The guitar group?
Status Quo

Q3
The trio's soundtrack TV album?
Rock Follies

Q4
Perry Como's Greatest Hits and Soul Motion came courtesy of
K-Tel

Q5
The year all this happened?
1976

QUIZ 189

QUIZ 191 SEVENTIES POP GENIUS

THE EYES HAVE IT

Five pairs of eyes to identify in this blinking easy round.

Q1
The Fleetwood Mac sticks man?
b Mick Fleetwood

Q2
Helping out when the band dynamic changed?
a Chester Thompson

Q3
Jones never played and recorded with
c Humble Pie

Q4
The drummer named on Déjà Vu was
a Dallas Taylor

Q5
Phil Rudd's nationality?
a Australian

QUESTION 1 *(4 POINTS)*
So easy we can't even clue you up on which sex.

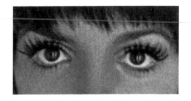

QUESTION 2 *(5 POINTS)*
Popular on both sides of the Atlantic.

QUESTION 3 *(5 POINTS)*
Folk hero from one of Britain's best-loved quartets.

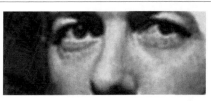

QUESTION 4 *(5 POINTS)*
A romantic view of a top talent.

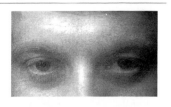

QUESTION 5 *(6 POINTS)*
Who is this seductive songstress?

SEVENTIES POP GENIUS QUIZ 192

THE PRICE IS RIGHT

In the early-70s, a loaf of bread would set you back 10p. But what of rock's essentials? Five questions testing your 70s buying habits.

QUESTION 1 *(5 POINTS)*
Which price is right? In 1971, a copy of rock weekly paper Sounds would have cost you how much?
a 6p
b 9p
c 12p

QUESTION 2 *(5 POINTS)*
In 1974, NME carried ads for fashion items called "Ziggy Jeans". These "famous jagger stitched" flares were priced at which figure?
a £1.99
b £3.25
c £5.90

QUESTION 3 *(5 POINTS)*
All 9,000 tickets sold out in less than an hour for a Wembley Arena Led Zeppelin gig in 1971. What was the price of a ticket?
a 75p
b £3.50
c £5.80

QUESTION 4 *(5 POINTS)*
And now to the price of the music itself. How much was the average price of a single back in 1973?
a 29p
b 48p
c 66p

QUESTION 5 *(5 POINTS)*
And finally, how much of a dent would an album make in your 1973 wallet or purse?
a 99p
b £1.73
c £2.34

Q1
'Good Ol' Boys' was the theme tune to The Dukes Of Hazzard

Q2
'Something Tells Me (Something Is Gonna Happen Tonight)' themed Cilla Black

Q3
The Rockford Files man was Mike Post (who also hit with The A-Team and Hill Street Blues)

Q4
'Theme From 'The Deer Hunter' (Cavatina)' went Top 10 for The Shadows

Q5
The Top 10 hit in question? 'Halfway Down The Stairs'

197

TRACKING DOWN THE WRITERS

The facts surrounding five songwriters who made a massive impact.

Q1 Liza Minnelli

QUESTION 1 *(5 POINTS)*

Rod Temperton wrote 'Boogie Nights' for his group Heatwave (and later wrote 'Thriller' for Michael Jackson), but where was he born?
a Lincolnshire, England
b Perth, Western Australia
c San Jose, California

Q2 Robert Plant

QUESTION 2 *(5 POINTS)*

Showaddywaddy's 70s single 'Three Steps To Heaven' was originally a No.1 hit for the song's writer in 1960. Name that writer.
a Gene Pitney
b Buddy Holly
c Eddie Cochran

Q3 Joe Strummer

QUESTION 3 *(5 POINTS)*

Who was the writing team responsible for the Carpenters' hit 'Top Of The World'?
a Karen Carpenter and John Bettis
b Richard Carpenter and John Bettis
c Neil Sedaka and John Bettis

Q4 Noddy Holder

QUESTION 4 *(5 POINTS)*

'The Killing Of Georgie' was Rod Stewart's biggest hit in 1976. Who wrote the ballad of a gay guy set upon by a New Jersey gang?
a Bruce Springsteen
b Tom Waits
c Rod Stewart

Q5 Linda Ronstadt

QUESTION 5 *(5 POINTS)*

Who penned Donny Osmond's 70s chart-topper 'Puppy Love'?
a Paul Williams
b Carole King
c Paul Anka

SEVENTIES POP GENIUS QUIZ 194

BABY, BABY, BABY

It's not hard to find pop songs "about my baby". Here are five questions to match.

QUIZ 192

QUESTION 1 *(5 POINTS)*
Who hit the Top 10 with 'My Baby Loves Lovin'?
a The Four Seasons
b White Plains
c Jimmy James and The Vagabonds

QUESTION 2 *(5 POINTS)*
Whose massive 1977 hit demanded 'Baby Don't Change Your Mind'?
a The Floaters
b Diana Ross
c Gladys Knight and The Pips

QUESTION 3 *(4 POINTS)*
The joys of impending parenthood is the subject of this 1974 hit. Who was the 'future dad' responsible for '(You're) Having My Baby'?
a Paul Simon
b Paul Anka
c Billy Paul

QUESTION 4 *(6 POINTS)*
In which year did the Bay City Rollers hit the top of the chart with 'Bye Bye Baby'?
a 1975
b 1976
c 1977

QUESTION 5 *(5 POINTS)*
Which mega Slade hit is introduced by Noddy Holder screeching "Baby, baby, baby!"
a 'Get Down And Get With It'
b 'Gudbuy T'Jane'
c 'Cum On Feel The Noize'

Q1
The cost of Sounds?
a 6p

Q2
The correct figure for flares?
b £3.25

Q3
The ticket price?
a 75p

Q4
The average cost?
b 48p

Q5
The dent in your 1973 wallet or purse?
c £2.34

QUIZ 193

THREE TRACK STATE OF MIND

Three tracks from a 70s studio album. Name the release they appear on.

Q1
Rod was born in
a Lincolnshire,
England

QUESTION 1 *(5 POINTS)*
'Wild Is The Wind', 'TVC 15' and 'Golden Years' are from which David Bowie album?

Q2
The songwriter
in question?
c Eddie Cochran

QUESTION 2 *(5 POINTS)*
'Dirty Little Girl', 'Grey Seal' and 'Candle In The Wind' are all included on which of Elton John's 70s studio albums?

Q3
The correct
writing team?
b Richard Carpenter
and John Bettis

QUESTION 3 *(5 POINTS)*
Which Black Sabbath album opens with 'Black Sabbath' followed by 'The Wizard' and 'Behind The Wall Of Sleep'?

Q4
The songwriter
was
c Rod Stewart

QUESTION 4 *(5 POINTS)*
'Coffee Homeground', 'Wow' and 'Hammer Horror' are all tracks on which Kate Bush album?

Q5
Donny Osmond's
70s chart-topper
was penned by
c Paul Anka

QUESTION 5 *(5 POINTS)*
'One After 909', 'Maggie Mae' and 'For You Blue' are all tracks from which 1970 chart-topper?

SEVENTIES POP GENIUS QUIZ 194

THE YEAR IS 1973

The year of The Exorcist, Some Mothers Do 'Ave 'Em and home power cuts also gave us some cracking music memories.

QUESTION 1 *(4 POINTS)*

Donny Osmond made No.1 with which date?
a 'The Twelfth Of Never'
b 'The Tenth Of Never'
c 'The First Of Never'

Q1
Hitting the Top
10 were
b White Plains

QUESTION 2 *(6 POINTS)*

Which piece of classical music is copied for Manfred Mann's Earth Band's Top 10 single 'Joybringer'?
a 'Jupiter' from Gustav Holst's Planet Suite
b The finale to Beethoven's Symphony No.3
c 'The Lark Ascending' from Vaughan Williams's The Four Seasons

Q2
Demanding 'Baby Don't Change Your Mind'?
c Gladys Knight and The Pips

QUESTION 3 *(6 POINTS)*

Which of these three was not a 1973 hit for The Faces?
a 'Pool Hall Richard' / 'I Wish It Would Rain'
b 'Stay With Me'
c 'Cindy Incidentally'

Q3
The 'future dad' was
b Paul Anka

QUESTION 4 *(4 POINTS)*

Complete the Billy Paul song title: 'Me And ____'.
a 'Me And The Lady'
b 'Me And You And A Dog Named Boo'
c 'Me And Mrs Jones'

Q4
'Bye Bye Baby' hit the top in
a 1975

QUESTION 5 *(5 POINTS)*

Which of these three had a 1973 hit with 'I'm Free'?
a The Who
b Electric Light Orchestra
c Roger Daltrey

Q5
The mega Slade hit?
c 'Cum On Feel The Noize'

QUIZ 197 SEVENTIES POP GENIUS

MYTHS, LEGENDS, WIVES AND JOURNEYS

Could be the title of Rick Wakeman's biography: five Rick questions.

Q1
The Bowie album in question?
Station To Station

QUESTION 1 *(5 POINTS)*
When Rick Wakeman joined Yes in 1971, who did he replace on keyboards?
a Al Stewart
b Tony Kaye
c Tony Banks

Q2
The Elton album?
Goodbye Yellow Brick Road

QUESTION 2 *(5 POINTS)*
He began his solo career with four Top 10 albums but which was the only one to top the chart?
a The Six Wives Of Henry VIII
b No Earthly Connection
c Journey To The Centre Of The Earth

Q3
The correct album title?
Black Sabbath

QUESTION 3 *(5 POINTS)*
Which of these three albums is a completely made-up title?
a White Rock
b The Wizard Of Prog
c Rick Wakeman's Criminal Record

Q4
All three tracks appeared on
Lionheart

QUESTION 4 *(5 POINTS)*
All Rick's 70s hit albums were released on the same record label. Which one?
a Virgin
b Atlantic
c A&M

Q5
The chart-topping album was
Let It Be by The Beatles

QUESTION 5 *(5 POINTS)*
In which year did Wakeman rejoin Yes for the recording of a new album, Going For The One?
a 1976
b 1978
c 1980

FIVE BIG ONES

Five single releases that resulted in the acts in question enjoying their peak performance in the 70s.

QUESTION 1 *(5 POINTS)*
Tom Jones managed seven chart hits during the decade, but which peaked highest at No.2 in 1971?
a 'She's A Lady'
b 'Something 'Bout You Baby I Like'
c 'Till'

Q1
The Donny date was
a 'The Twelfth Of Never'

QUESTION 2 *(4 POINTS)*
All of Don McLean's three 70s hits are here. Just choose the highest placed – a chart-topper in 1972.
a 'Vincent'
b 'American Pie'
c 'Everyday'

Q2
The classical piece in question?
a 'Jupiter' from Gustav Holst's Planet Suite

QUESTION 3 *(5 POINTS)*
Pick one from three from The Three Degrees' back catalogue. Their only 70s No.1 came in 1974 with what?
a 'My Simple Heart'
b 'When Will I See You Again'
c 'Take Good Care Of Yourself'

Q3
Not a 1973 hit for The Faces?
b 'Stay With Me' which peaked at No.6 in 1971

QUESTION 4 *(5 POINTS)*
The Real Thing enjoyed nine 70s hits. One even made it to the top spot in 1976, but which one?
a 'Can You Feel The Force?'
b 'You To Me Are Everything'
c 'Boogie Down (Get Funky Now)'

Q4
The complete Billy Paul song title is
c 'Me And Mrs Jones'

QUESTION 5 *(6 POINTS)*
One of these three Charlie Rich hits was far and away his biggest success, peaking at No.2 in 1974.
a 'Behind Closed Doors'
b 'We Love Each Other'
c 'The Most Beautiful Girl'

Q5
'I'm Free' went Top 3 for
c Roger Daltrey

QUIZ 197

Q1
Wakeman replaced
b Tony Kaye

Q2
The chart-topper?
c Journey To The Centre Of The Earth

Q3
The completely made-up title?
b The Wizard Of Prog

Q4
The record label was
c A&M

Q5
The year in question?
a 1976

NEWS CLUES

Three memorable facts that made news and pop headlines for a mystery year in each of these five questions.

QUESTION 1 *(5 POINTS)*
Argentina win the World Cup, the world's first 'test-tube baby' is born and Rumours by Fleetwood Mac tops the album chart. The year is?

QUESTION 2 *(5 POINTS)*
Bulgarian defector Georgi Markov dies after being stabbed by a poisoned umbrella in London, Superman flies onto UK cinema screens and 'Figaro' is No.1 for Brotherhood Of Man. The year is?

QUESTION 3 *(5 POINTS)*
'December, 1963 (Oh What A Night)' is a surprise No.1 for The Four Seasons, Bjorn Borg becomes Wimbledon men's tennis champion (defeating Ilie Nastase in the final) and Steve Jobs and Stephen Wozniak start the Apple computer company. The year is?

QUESTION 4 *(5 POINTS)*
The UK voting age is reduced from 21 to 18, Oh! Calcutta brings nudity to London's West End and 'Spirit In The Sky' is a spring No.1 for Norman Greenbaum. The year is?

QUESTION 5 *(5 POINTS)*
LBC, Britain's first commercial radio station, is launched, Alice Cooper's Billion Dollar Babies sits at the top of the album chart and Ronnie Lane leaves The Faces to form Slim Chance. The year is?

SEVENTIES POP GENIUS QUIZ 200

THE FINAL COUNTDOWN

Fittingly, this last 70s quiz uses the final Top 40 chart of the decade as its subject matter.

QUIZ 198

QUESTION 1 *(4 POINTS)*

Racing up the singles chart as the month, year and decade come to an end is a day trip to which destination by Fiddler's Dram?

a 'Day Trip To Bangor'
b 'Day Trip To Blackpool'
c 'Day Trip To Bordeaux'

Q1
Tom Jones's 70s peak hit?
c 'Till'

QUESTION 2 *(5 POINTS)*

What was the significant fact about the arrival on the scene of Sugarhill Gang's 'Rapper's Delight'?

a It was the first record to hit the singles chart with no vinyl release.
b It was the first rap record to make a big impact.
c It was released by the (then) youngest group ever to make the Top 10.

Q2
The Don McLean chart-topper in 1972?
a 'Vincent'

QUESTION 3 *(5 POINTS)*

The catchy 'Que Sera Mi Vida (If You Should Go)' was No.8 in the decade's final chart. The Martiniquan brothers responsible?

a The Blues Brothers
b The Mills Brothers
c The Gibson Brothers

Q3
No.1 for The Three Degrees was
b 'When Will I See You Again'

QUESTION 4 *(5 POINTS)*

Issued in 1979 'John, I'm Only Dancing (Again)' was a reworking by David Bowie of his earlier No.12 hit from which year?

a 1969
b 1972
c 1975

Q4
The Real Thing single that made it to the top?
b 'You To Me Are Everything'

QUESTION 5 *(6 POINTS)*

'It's My House' was a modest hit in the decade's final chart for two acts. Diana Ross was one, but who was the other?

a Storm
b Rose Royce
c The Elgins

Q5
Charlie's biggest hit was
c 'The Most Beautiful Girl'

THE ULTIMATE ROCK GUIDE

To answer the questions below and find out about 694 other locations worthy of pilgrimage in Britain and Ireland you'll need 'Rock Atlas' by David Roberts. Packed with facts about rock music including album cover locations, historic gigs, memorials, statues and much, much more!

Where can I shop in the world's oldest record store?

How do I find the Jimi Hendrix statue?

Where is the real Stawberry Field?

Which famous park has a musical bench in memory of Ian Dury?

Where is the spooky location for 1970s' Black Sabbath album cover?

In which pub did The Arctic Monkeys make their debut?

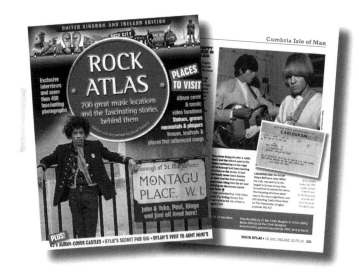

On sale now

For information on Clarksdale books visit www.clarksdalebooks.co.uk

Q1
Argentina, 'test-tube baby' and Rumours all point to
1978

Q2
Georgi Markov, Superman and 'Figaro'?
It must be
1978

Q3
A Four Seasons No.1, Bjorn Borg and the start of Apple computers?
1976

Q4
A voting change, Oh! Calcutta and 'Spirit In The Sky'?
1970

Q5
LBC launched, Billion Dollar Babies and a Faces departure?
1973

500 LOST GEMS

We have a number of collectors copies still available of the limited, numbered hardback edition of 500 Lost Gems of the Sixties. Beautifully designed and printed on high quality paper in full colour this book is a must for record collectors.

SAVE £5.75 (while stocks last)

To order your copy visit:
www.clarksdalebooks.co.uk
At checkout enter code: QUIZ 98H

Q1
The decade-ending destination?
a 'Day Trip To Bangor'

Q2
The significant fact?
b It was the first rap record to make a big impact

Q3
The Martiniquan brothers were
c The Gibson Brothers

Q4
This David Bowie hit was originally from
b 1972

Q5
The 'other' chart act was
a Storm

The delta town of Clarksdale, Mississippi
is the self-appointed 'home of the blues'. It
stands at the crossroads. Not just any random
intersection but *The Crossroads*. That dusty,
sun-parched junction where the old Highways
49 and 61cross.

Highway 61... the Blues Highway that for
generations of black musicians promised
fame and fortune – the route that linked New
Orleans to Chicago; or Highway 49 leading
straight back into Clarksdale... and life back in
the cottonfields.

There are many legends in the blues about
crossroads and one has Robert Johnson
making a Faustian pact with the devil at the
Clarksdale crossroads.

What is certain is that the choices made at the
crossroads could shape a man's life.

CLARKSDALE
www.clarksdalebooks.co.uk

Printed in Great Britain
by Amazon.co.uk, Ltd.,
Marston Gate.